C000119271

The Open University

I3

Number systems

This publication forms part of an Open University course. Details of this and other Open University courses can be obtained from the Student Registration and Enquiry Service, The Open University, PO Box 197, Milton Keynes, MK7 6BJ, United Kingdom: tel. +44 (0)870 333 4340, e-mail general-enquiries@open.ac.uk

Alternatively, you may visit the Open University website at http://www.open.ac.uk where you can learn more about the wide range of courses and packs offered at all levels by The Open University.

To purchase a selection of Open University course materials, visit the webshop at www.ouw.co.uk, or contact Open University Worldwide, Michael Young Building, Walton Hall, Milton Keynes, MK7 6AA, United Kingdom, for a brochure: tel. +44 (0)1908 858785, fax +44 (0)1908 858787, e-mail ouwenq@open.ac.uk

The Open University, Walton Hall, Milton Keynes, MK7 6AA.

First published 2006.

Edited, designed and typeset by The Open University, using the Open University TEX System.

Printed and bound in the United Kingdom by Hobbs the Printers Limited, Brunel Road, Totton, Hampshire SO40 3WX.

ISBN 0 7492 0206 8

1.1

Contents

Introduction

In this unit we look at some different systems of numbers, and the rules for combining numbers in these systems. You will have met many of these systems before, and you will meet some of them in more detail later in the course.

In particular, for each system we consider the question of which elements have additive and/or multiplicative inverses in the system. We look at solving certain equations in the system, such as linear, quadratic and other polynomial equations.

In Section 1 we start by revising the notation used for the *rational numbers* and the *real numbers*, and we list their arithmetical properties. You will meet other properties of these numbers in the analysis units, as the study of real functions depends on properties of the real numbers. We note that some quadratic equations with rational coefficients, such as $x^2 = 2$, have solutions which are real but not rational.

In Section 2 we introduce the set of *complex numbers*. This system of numbers enables us to solve *all* polynomial equations, including those with no real solutions, such as $x^2 + 1 = 0$. Just as real numbers correspond to points on the real line, so complex numbers correspond to points in a plane, known as the *complex plane*.

In Section 3 we look further at some properties of the *integers*, and introduce *modular arithmetic*. This will be useful in the group theory units, as some sets of numbers with the operation of modular addition or modular multiplication form *groups*.

In Section 4 we introduce the concept of a *relation* between elements of a set. This is a more general idea than that of a function, and leads us to a mathematical structure known as an *equivalence relation*. An equivalence relation on a set classifies elements of the set, separating them into disjoint subsets called *equivalence classes*.

Study guide

Sections 1–4 should ideally be studied in their natural order, although it is possible to study Section 3 at any time after Section 1.

Section 1 is a short revision section, which should not take too much time.

Section 2 is a long section introducing many concepts, some or all of which may be new to you. There are many exercises in this section and you may not have time to do them all. We suggest that you concentrate on the exercises, or the parts of the exercises, in which you most need practice.

Section 3 may seem more familiar. The section on multiplicative inverses is probably the most difficult part.

Section 4 is a short section, but you may find it less straightforward than the earlier sections. The results relate back to Section 3 and will also be important in the group theory blocks.

1   Real numbers

After working through this section, you should be able to:

understand the arithmetical properties of the rational and real numbers.

1.1 Rational numbers

In Unit I2 you met the sets

$\mathbb{N} = \{1, 2, 3, \ldots\}$, the natural numbers;

$\mathbb{Z} = \{\ldots, -2, -1, 0, 1, 2, \ldots\}$, the integers;

$\mathbb{Q} = \{p/q : p \in \mathbb{Z}, q \in \mathbb{N}\}$, the rational numbers.

Notice that each set in this list is a subset of the succeeding one; that is,

$\mathbb{N} \subseteq \mathbb{Z}$ and $\mathbb{Z} \subseteq \mathbb{Q}$.

$\mathbb{Q}$ is the set of numbers that can be written as fractions, such as $\frac{3}{4}$ and $-1.7 = -\frac{17}{10}$.

To represent the rational numbers geometrically, we use a number line. We begin by drawing a line and marking on it points corresponding to the integers 0 and 1. If the distance between 0 and 1 is taken as a unit of length, then the rational numbers can be arranged on the line in a natural order. For example, the rational 4/3 is placed at the point which is one third of the distance from 1 to 2.

We sometimes use 'rational' as shorthand for 'rational number' and 'real' for 'real number'.

Each rational number also has a decimal representation, which is either a terminating (that is, finite) decimal, such as 1.54, or a recurring decimal such as $2.134\,734\,734\,7\ldots$, in which the digits repeat in a regular pattern from some position onwards. The decimal representation of any rational number p/q can be obtained by using long division to divide q into p.

One of the surprising mathematical discoveries made by the ancient Greeks was that the system of rational numbers is not adequate to describe all the lengths that occur in geometry. For example, consider the diagonal of a square of side 1. What is its length? If the length is x, then, by Pythagoras' Theorem, x must satisfy the equation $x^2 = 2$. However, there is no rational number that satisfies this equation.

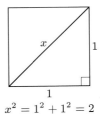

$x^2 = 1^2 + 1^2 = 2$

Theorem 1.1   There is no rational number x such that $x^2 = 2$.

Proof   Suppose that such a rational number x exists. Then we can write $x = p/q$, where $p, q \in \mathbb{N}$. By cancelling, if necessary, we may assume that the greatest common factor of p and q is 1.

This is a proof by contradiction.

There is a reminder of the definition of *greatest common factor* on page 36.

The equation $x^2 = 2$ now becomes

$$\frac{p^2}{q^2} = 2,$$

so

$$p^2 = 2q^2. \tag{1.1}$$

The square of an odd number is odd, so p cannot be odd. Hence p is even, so we can write $p = 2r$, say. Equation (1.1) now becomes

$$(2r)^2 = 2q^2,$$

so

$$q^2 = 2r^2.$$

We have
$$(2k+1)^2 = 4k^2 + 4k + 1$$
$$= 4(k^2 + k) + 1.$$

Reasoning as before, we find that q is also even.

Since p and q are both even, they have a common factor of 2, which contradicts our earlier statement that the greatest common factor of p and q is 1.

Since we have obtained a contradiction, our original assumption must be false; therefore no such rational number x exists. ∎

> **Exercise 1.1**   By imitating the proof above, show that there is no rational number x such that $x^3 = 2$.

Since we expect equations such as $x^2 = 2$ and $x^3 = 2$ to have solutions, we must introduce new numbers that are not rationals. We denote the positive solutions of these two equations by $\sqrt{2}$ and $\sqrt[3]{2}$, respectively; thus $(\sqrt{2})^2 = 2$ and $(\sqrt[3]{2})^3 = 2$. Of course, we must introduce many other new numbers, such as $\sqrt{3}$, $\sqrt{7}$, and so on. Indeed, it can be shown that if m and n are natural numbers, and the equation $x^m = n$ has no integer solution, then the positive solution of this equation, written as $\sqrt[m]{n}$, cannot be rational.

The case $m = 2$ and $n = 3$ is treated in Exercise 1.5.

There are many other mathematical quantities which cannot be described exactly by rational numbers. For example, the number π, which denotes the area of a disc of radius 1 (or half the length of the perimeter of such a disc), cannot be described by a rational number, and neither can the number e.

Johann Heinrich Lambert proved in 1761 that π is irrational. He was a colleague of Euler and Lagrange at the Berlin Academy of Sciences, and is best known for his work on π.

All these numbers are known as **irrational** numbers.

1.2 Real numbers

The rational and irrational numbers together make up the **real** numbers. The set of real numbers is denoted by $\mathbb{R}$. Like rationals, irrational numbers can be represented by decimals, but unlike the decimals for rational numbers, those for irrationals are neither finite nor recurring. All such infinite non-recurring decimals represent real numbers. Each real number can be represented as a point on the number line considered in Section 1.1, which is often known as the **real line**, and each point on this line represents a real number.

We shall need to use the usual arithmetical operations on real numbers, and we now list the properties which we assume these operations satisfy.

Arithmetic in $\mathbb{R}$

Addition	Multiplication	
A1. If $a, b \in \mathbb{R}$, then $a + b \in \mathbb{R}$.	M1. If $a, b \in \mathbb{R}$, then $a \times b \in \mathbb{R}$.	CLOSURE
A2. If $a \in \mathbb{R}$, then $a + 0 = 0 + a = a$.	M2. If $a \in \mathbb{R}$, then $a \times 1 = 1 \times a = a$.	IDENTITY
A3. If $a \in \mathbb{R}$, then there is a number $-a \in \mathbb{R}$ such that $a + (-a) = (-a) + a = 0$.	M3. If $a \in \mathbb{R} - \{0\}$, then there is a number $a^{-1} \in \mathbb{R}$ such that $a \times a^{-1} = a^{-1} \times a = 1$.	INVERSES
A4. If $a, b, c \in \mathbb{R}$, then $(a + b) + c = a + (b + c)$.	M4. If $a, b, c \in \mathbb{R}$, then $(a \times b) \times c = a \times (b \times c)$.	ASSOCIATIVITY
A5. If $a, b \in \mathbb{R}$, then $a + b = b + a$.	M5. If $a, b \in \mathbb{R}$, then $a \times b = b \times a$.	COMMUTATIVITY
D. If $a, b, c \in \mathbb{R}$, then $a \times (b + c) = a \times b + a \times c$.		DISTRIBUTIVITY

In properties A3 and M3 the numbers $-a$ and a^{-1} are known as the *additive inverse* (or *negative*) of a and the *multiplicative inverse* (or *reciprocal*) of a, respectively.

The rational numbers $\mathbb{Q}$ also satisfy all the above properties; that is, if $\mathbb{R}$ is replaced by $\mathbb{Q}$ throughout in the box above, then the properties are still true. We shall show later that the same is true for the complex numbers $\mathbb{C}$ and for some sets of numbers in modular arithmetic. However, if we restrict ourselves to the integers $\mathbb{Z}$, then one of these properties is no longer true.

A set with all these properties is known as a *field*.

Exercise 1.2

(a) Show by means of a counter-example that $\mathbb{Z}$ does not have property M3.

(b) Which integers have a multiplicative inverse in $\mathbb{Z}$?

In this unit we shall be concerned with *polynomial equations*.

Definition A **polynomial equation** in x of degree n is an equation of the form $p(x) = 0$, where $p(x)$ is a polynomial of degree n.

Polynomial equations (and polynomials) of degrees 1, 2 and 3 are called *linear*, *quadratic* and *cubic*, respectively.

Exercise 1.3 Solve the following quadratic equations, stating how many solutions each equation has in $\mathbb{R}$.

(a) $x^2 - 7x + 12 = 0$

(b) $x^2 + 6x + 9 = 0$

(c) $2x^2 + 5x - 3 = 0$

(d) $2x^2 - 2x - 1 = 0$

(e) $x^2 - 2x + 5 = 0$

Recall that the formula for the solutions of the quadratic equation $ax^2 + bx + c = 0$ is
$$x = \frac{-b \pm \sqrt{b^2 - 4ac}}{2a}.$$
This equation is known as the *quadratic formula*.

We notice from the results of Exercise 1.3 that some quadratic equations have two real solutions, some have only one and some have none. In either of the first two cases, the solutions may be rational or irrational. Although you may be accustomed to equations with integer coefficients such as those in Exercise 1.3, these results still apply if some or all of the coefficients are irrational; that is, if the coefficients are any real numbers. Since a quadratic equation with coefficients in $\mathbb{R}$ can have no solution in $\mathbb{R}$, working with the set of real numbers does not enable us to find solutions to all quadratic equations.

We end this section by showing that although a quadratic equation may have no real solutions, this is not true for a cubic equation.

Consider the cubic polynomial

$$ax^3 + bx^2 + cx + d, \quad \text{where } a > 0.$$

For $x \neq 0$, the polynomial can be written as

$$x^3 \left(a + \frac{b}{x} + \frac{c}{x^2} + \frac{d}{x^3} \right).$$

Since $\dfrac{1}{x}, \dfrac{1}{x^2}$ and $\dfrac{1}{x^3} \to 0$ as $x \to \infty$, the sign of the polynomial will be positive when x is large and positive, and negative when x is large and negative. Hence the value of the polynomial must change from negative to positive at least once as x increases, so it would appear that it must be zero at one value of x (at least). A similar argument can be used if $a < 0$. Hence the equation $ax^3 + bx^2 + cx + d = 0$, where $a \neq 0$, has at least one real solution. This result can be generalised to show that any polynomial equation of degree n, where n is odd, has at least one real solution.

We are assuming here that the graph of a cubic polynomial is an unbroken curve—an assumption we made in Unit I1. This assumption will be justified in the analysis units.

Further exercises

Exercise 1.4   Solve the following linear equations.

(a) $5x + 8 = -2$ (b) $\sqrt{3}x + 2 = -5$

(c) $2x - 1 = 5$ (d) $5x + 4 = 3$

State in each case whether the solution belongs to $\mathbb{N}$, $\mathbb{Z}$, $\mathbb{Q}$ and/or $\mathbb{R}$.

Exercise 1.5   Show that there is no rational number x such that $x^2 = 3$.

2   Complex numbers

After working through this section, you should be able to:

(a) understand the definition of a *complex number*;
(b) perform arithmetical operations with complex numbers;
(c) represent complex numbers as points in the *complex plane*;
(d) determine the *polar form* of a complex number;
(e) use *de Moivre's Theorem* to find the nth roots of a complex number and to find some trigonometric identities;
(f) understand the definition of e^z, where z is a complex variable.

In this section we discuss complex numbers and their properties. We show how they can be represented as points in the plane. We state the Fundamental Theorem of Algebra: that any polynomial equation with complex coefficients has a solution which is a complex number. We define the function exp of a complex variable.

2.1   What is a complex number?

Earlier we mentioned several sets of numbers, including $\mathbb{N}$, $\mathbb{Z}$, $\mathbb{Q}$ and $\mathbb{R}$. In each case, the numbers correspond to points on the real line. We now introduce numbers of a new kind, the so-called *complex numbers*, which correspond to points in the plane.

Complex numbers arise naturally as solutions of quadratic equations. For example, you showed in Exercise 1.3(e) that the equation $x^2 - 2x + 5 = 0$ has no real solutions because there is no real number whose square is -16.

But suppose now that we 'extend' the set of real numbers by introducing a new number, denoted by i, which is defined to have the property that $i^2 = -1$. Suppose further that i combines with itself, and with real numbers, according to the usual rules of arithmetic. In particular, assume that we can multiply i by any real number b to obtain the product ib, and that we can add on any real number a to obtain the sum $a + ib$. Such sums are known as *complex numbers*, and they are the numbers we need to solve the quadratic equation above.

We have $ib = bi$, and we can also write $a + ib$ as $a + bi$.

Definitions   A **complex number** is an expression of the form $x + iy$, where x and y are real numbers and $i^2 = -1$. The set of all complex numbers is denoted by $\mathbb{C}$.

A complex number $z = x + iy$ has **real part** x and **imaginary part** y; we write

$$\operatorname{Re} z = x \quad \text{and} \quad \operatorname{Im} z = y.$$

Two complex numbers are equal when their real parts *and* their imaginary parts are equal.

For example, if $z = 2 - 3i$, then $\operatorname{Re} z = 2$ and $\operatorname{Im} z = -3$.

Remarks

1. Any given real number x can be written in the form $x + i0$, and any complex number of the form $x + i0$ is usually written simply as x. In this sense, $\mathbb{R}$ is a subset of $\mathbb{C}$. The zero complex number $0 + i0$ is written as 0.

2. We usually write a general complex number as $x + iy$, and a particular complex number as, for example, $2 + 3i$, rather than $2 + i3$.

   We write $2 - 3i$ rather than $2 + (-3)i$.

3. Note that $\operatorname{Re} z$ and $\operatorname{Im} z$ are both real numbers.

4. A complex number of the form $0 + iy$ (where $y \neq 0$) is sometimes called an *imaginary number*.

Since $i^2 = -1$, we can regard the number i as a square root of -1. If we assume that the usual rules of arithmetic apply, then we can solve quadratic equations using the quadratic formula and the fact that $\sqrt{-1} = i$. For example, consider the equation

$$z^2 - 2z + 5 = 0.$$

This is the equation from Exercise 1.3(e), rewritten using z as the variable name. We often use the letter z for a complex variable (a variable that represents a complex number).

For the above equation, the quadratic formula gives

$$z = \frac{2 \pm \sqrt{-16}}{2} = \frac{2 \pm \sqrt{16}\sqrt{-1}}{2} = \frac{2 \pm 4i}{2} = 1 \pm 2i.$$

We can check that these two complex numbers satisfy the equation we were trying to solve. We use the usual rules of arithmetic, and substitute -1 for i^2 wherever it appears.

For example, if $z = 1 + 2i$, then

$$
\begin{aligned}
z^2 - 2z + 5 &= (1 + 2i)^2 - 2(1 + 2i) + 5 \\
&= 1 + 4i + 4i^2 - 2 - 4i + 5 \\
&= 1 + 4i - 4 - 2 - 4i + 5 \\
&= 0.
\end{aligned}
$$

$4i^2 = 4(-1) = -4$, since $i^2 = -1$.

The solution $z = 1 - 2i$ can be checked similarly.

The use of the number i enables us to solve any quadratic equation in a similar way. We shall see later in the section that the use of i ensures that all polynomial equations have solutions, even those whose coefficients are themselves complex. This, in turn, means that any polynomial can be factorised into a product of linear factors; for example,

$$z^2 - 2z + 5 = (z - (1 + 2i))(z - (1 - 2i)) = (z - 1 - 2i)(z - 1 + 2i).$$

Exercise 2.1   Solve the following equations, giving all solutions in $\mathbb{C}$.

(a) $z^2 - 4z + 7 = 0$

(b) $z^2 - iz + 2 = 0$

(c) $z^3 - 3z^2 + 4z - 2 = 0$ (Hint: $z = 1$ is one solution.)

(d) $z^4 - 16 = 0$

The complex plane

Just as there is a one-one correspondence between the real numbers and the points on the real line, so there is a one-one correspondence between the complex numbers and the points in the plane. This correspondence is given by

$$f\colon \mathbb{C} \longrightarrow \mathbb{R}^2$$
$$x + iy \longmapsto (x, y).$$

Thus we can represent points in the plane by complex numbers and, conversely, we can represent complex numbers by points in the plane. When we represent complex numbers by points in the plane, we refer to the plane as the **complex plane**, and we often refer to the complex numbers as *points* in the complex plane. A diagram showing complex numbers represented as points in the plane in this way is sometimes called an **Argand diagram**.

Real numbers are represented in the complex plane by points on the x-axis; this axis is called the *real axis*. Similarly, numbers of the form iy are represented by points on the y-axis; this axis is called the *imaginary axis*.

The French mathematician Jean-Robert Argand's publication of the idea in 1806 was the first to be generally recognised.

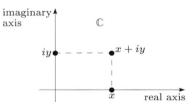

> **Exercise 2.2**   Draw a diagram showing each of the following points in the complex plane:
>
> $$2 + 3i, \quad -3 + 2i, \quad -2 - i, \quad 3 - 2i.$$

Complex arithmetic

Arithmetical operations on complex numbers are carried out as for real numbers, except that we replace i^2 by -1 wherever it occurs.

Example 2.1   Let $z_1 = 1 + 2i$ and $z_2 = 3 - 4i$. Determine the following complex numbers.

(a) $z_1 + z_2$ (b) $z_1 - z_2$ (c) $z_1 z_2$ (d) z_1^2

Solution   Using the usual rules of arithmetic, with the additional property that $i^2 = -1$, we obtain the following.

(a) $z_1 + z_2 = (1 + 2i) + (3 - 4i) = (1 + 3) + (2 - 4)i = 4 - 2i$

(b) $z_1 - z_2 = (1 + 2i) - (3 - 4i) = (1 - 3) + (2 + 4)i = -2 + 6i$

(c) $z_1 z_2 = (1 + 2i)(3 - 4i) = 3 + 6i - 4i - 8i^2 = 3 + 2i + 8 = 11 + 2i$

(d) $z_1^2 = (1 + 2i)(1 + 2i) = 1 + 2i + 2i + 4i^2 = 1 + 4i - 4 = -3 + 4i$ ∎

> **Exercise 2.3**   Determine the following complex numbers.
>
> (a) $(3 - 5i) + (2 + 4i)$ (b) $(2 - 3i)(-3 + 2i)$
>
> (c) $(5 + 3i)^2$ (d) $(1 + i)(7 + 2i)(4 - i)$

Example 2.1 illustrates how we add, subtract and multiply two given complex numbers. We can apply the same methods to two general complex numbers $z_1 = x_1 + iy_1$ and $z_2 = x_2 + iy_2$, and obtain the following formal definitions of addition, subtraction and multiplication in $\mathbb{C}$.

Definitions   Let $z_1 = x_1 + iy_1$ and $z_2 = x_2 + iy_2$ be any complex numbers. Then the following operations can be applied.

addition	$z_1 + z_2 = (x_1 + x_2) + i(y_1 + y_2)$
subtraction	$z_1 - z_2 = (x_1 - x_2) + i(y_1 - y_2)$
multiplication	$z_1 z_2 = (x_1 x_2 - y_1 y_2) + i(x_1 y_2 + y_1 x_2)$

With these definitions, most of the usual rules of algebra still hold, as do many of the familiar algebraic identities. For example,
$$(z_1 + z_2)^2 = z_1^2 + 2z_1 z_2 + z_2^2$$
and
$$z_1^2 - z_2^2 = (z_1 - z_2)(z_1 + z_2).$$

There is no need to remember or look up these formulas. For calculations, the methods of Example 2.1 may be used.

An obvious omission from this list of definitions is *division*. We return to division after discussing the *complex conjugate* and *modulus* of a complex number.

Complex conjugate

Many manipulations involving complex numbers, such as division, can be simplified by using the idea of a *complex conjugate*, which we now introduce.

Definition   The **complex conjugate** $\overline{z}$ of the complex number $z = x + iy$ is the complex number $x - iy$.

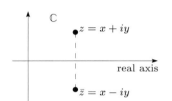

For example, if $z = 1 - 2i$, then $\overline{z} = 1 + 2i$. In geometric terms, $\overline{z}$ is the image of z under reflection in the real axis.

> **Exercise 2.4**   Let $z_1 = -2 + 3i$ and $z_2 = 3 - i$. Write down $\overline{z_1}$ and $\overline{z_2}$, and draw a diagram showing z_1, z_2, $\overline{z_1}$ and $\overline{z_2}$ in the complex plane.

The following properties of complex conjugates are particularly useful.

Properties of complex conjugates   Let z_1, z_2 and z be any complex numbers. Then:
1. $\overline{z_1 + z_2} = \overline{z_1} + \overline{z_2}$;
2. $\overline{z_1 z_2} = \overline{z_1} \times \overline{z_2}$;
3. $z + \overline{z} = 2\operatorname{Re} z$;
4. $z - \overline{z} = 2i\operatorname{Im} z$.

In order to prove property 1, we consider two arbitrary complex numbers. Let $z_1 = x_1 + iy_1$ and $z_2 = x_2 + iy_2$. Then
$$
\begin{aligned}
\overline{z_1 + z_2} &= \overline{(x_1 + x_2) + i(y_1 + y_2)} \\
&= (x_1 + x_2) - i(y_1 + y_2) \\
&= (x_1 - iy_1) + (x_2 - iy_2) \\
&= \overline{z_1} + \overline{z_2}.
\end{aligned}
$$

> **Exercise 2.5**   Use a similar approach to prove properties 2, 3 and 4.

Modulus of a complex number

We also need the idea of the *modulus* of a complex number. Recall that the modulus of a real number x is defined by

$$|x| = \begin{cases} x & \text{if } x \geq 0, \\ -x & \text{if } x < 0. \end{cases}$$

For example, $|7| = 7$ and $|-6| = 6$.

In other words, $|x|$ is the distance from the point x on the real line to the origin. We extend this definition to complex numbers as follows.

Definition   The **modulus** $|z|$ of a complex number z is the distance from the point z in the complex plane to the origin.

Thus the modulus of the complex number $z = x + iy$ is

$$|z| = \sqrt{x^2 + y^2}.$$

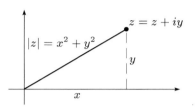

For example, if $z = 3 - 4i$, then $|z| = \sqrt{3^2 + (-4)^2} = \sqrt{25} = 5$.

> **Exercise 2.6**   Determine the modulus of each of the following complex numbers.
> (a) $5 + 12i$ (b) $1 + i$ (c) -5

The modulus of a complex number has many properties similar to those of the modulus of a real number.

Properties of modulus
1. $|z| \geq 0$ for any $z \in \mathbb{C}$, with equality only when $z = 0$.
2. $|z_1 z_2| = |z_1| \, |z_2|$ for any $z_1, z_2 \in \mathbb{C}$.

Property 1 is clear from the definition of $|z|$. Property 2 can be proved in a similar way to property 2 of complex conjugates given on page 12.

The following useful result shows the link between modulus and distance in the complex plane.

Distance Formula   The distance between the points z_1 and z_2 in the complex plane is $|z_1 - z_2|$.

This is obtained by applying Pythagoras' Theorem to the triangle in the diagram below.

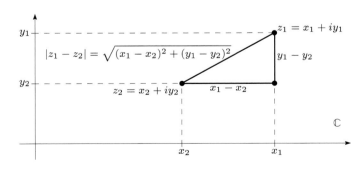

Exercise 2.7   For each of the following pairs z_1, z_2 of complex numbers, draw a diagram showing z_1 and z_2 in the complex plane, and evaluate $|z_1 - z_2|$.

(a) $z_1 = 3 + i$, $z_2 = 1 + 2i$.

(b) $z_1 = 1$, $z_2 = i$.

(c) $z_1 = -5 - 3i$, $z_2 = 2 - 7i$.

The following properties describe the relationship between the modulus and the complex conjugate of a complex number.

Conjugate–modulus properties

1. $|\overline{z}| = |z|$ for all $z \in \mathbb{C}$.
2. $z\overline{z} = |z|^2$ for all $z \in \mathbb{C}$.

To prove these properties, we let $z = x + iy$. Then $\overline{z} = x - iy = x + i(-y)$, so

$$|\overline{z}| = \sqrt{x^2 + (-y)^2} = \sqrt{x^2 + y^2} = |z|$$

and

$$z\overline{z} = (x + iy)(x - iy) = x^2 + ixy - ixy - i^2 y^2 = x^2 + y^2 = |z|^2.$$

Division of complex numbers

The second of the conjugate–modulus properties enables us to find reciprocals of complex numbers and to divide one complex number by another, as shown in the next example. As for real numbers, we cannot find a reciprocal of zero, nor divide any complex number by zero.

Example 2.2

(a) Find the reciprocal of $2 - 5i$.

(b) Find the quotient $\dfrac{3 - i}{1 + 2i}$.

Solution

(a) We want to find the complex number which represents $\dfrac{1}{2 - 5i}$.

We multiply the numerator and denominator by $2 + 5i$, the complex conjugate of $2 - 5i$, to give

$$\frac{1}{2 - 5i} = \frac{1(2 + 5i)}{(2 - 5i)(2 + 5i)} = \frac{2 + 5i}{4 - 25i^2} = \frac{2 + 5i}{4 + 25} = \tfrac{2}{29} + \tfrac{5}{29}i.$$

(b) We multiply the numerator and denominator by $1 - 2i$, the complex conjugate of $1 + 2i$, to give

$$\frac{3 - i}{1 + 2i} = \frac{(3 - i)(1 - 2i)}{(1 + 2i)(1 - 2i)} = \frac{3 - i - 6i + 2i^2}{1 - 4i^2} = \frac{1 - 7i}{1 + 4} = \tfrac{1}{5} - \tfrac{7}{5}i. \quad \blacksquare$$

The method used in Example 2.2, of multiplying the numerator and denominator by the complex conjugate of the denominator, enables us to find the reciprocal of any non-zero complex number z, and the quotient z_1/z_2 of any two complex numbers z_1 and z_2, where $z_2 \neq 0$. We can obtain general formulas as follows.

For the reciprocal, we have

$$\frac{1}{z} = \frac{1 \times \overline{z}}{z \times \overline{z}} = \frac{\overline{z}}{|z|^2}, \quad \text{for } z \neq 0.$$

If $z = x + iy$, so $\overline{z} = x - iy$ and $|z|^2 = x^2 + y^2$, we obtain

$$\frac{1}{x + iy} = \frac{x - iy}{x^2 + y^2}.$$

For the quotient z_1/z_2, we have

$$\frac{z_1}{z_2} = \frac{z_1 \times \overline{z_2}}{z_2 \times \overline{z_2}} = \frac{z_1 \overline{z_2}}{|z_2|^2}, \quad \text{for } z_2 \neq 0.$$

If $z_1 = x_1 + iy_1$ and $z_2 = x_2 + iy_2$, this can be rewritten as

$$\frac{x_1 + iy_1}{x_2 + iy_2} = \frac{(x_1 + iy_1)(x_2 - iy_2)}{x_2^2 + y_2^2} = \frac{(x_1 x_2 + y_1 y_2) + i(y_1 x_2 - x_1 y_2)}{x_2^2 + y_2^2}.$$

These formulas may be used in theoretical work, but for calculations of reciprocals and quotients it is simplest to use the method of Example 2.2.

Exercise 2.8 Find the reciprocal of each of the following complex numbers.

(a) $3 - i$ (b) $-1 + 2i$

Exercise 2.9 Evaluate each of the following quotients.

(a) $\dfrac{5}{2 - i}$ (b) $\dfrac{2 + 3i}{-3 + 4i}$

Arithmetical properties of complex numbers

The set of complex numbers $\mathbb{C}$ satisfies all the properties previously given for arithmetic in $\mathbb{R}$. We state (but do not prove) these properties here.

Arithmetic in $\mathbb{C}$

Addition

A1. If $z_1, z_2 \in \mathbb{C}$, then
$z_1 + z_2 \in \mathbb{C}$.

A2. If $z \in \mathbb{C}$, then
$z + 0 = 0 + z = z$.

A3. If $z \in \mathbb{C}$, then there
is a number $-z \in \mathbb{C}$
such that
$z + (-z) = (-z) + z = 0$.

A4. If $z_1, z_2, z_3 \in \mathbb{C}$, then
$(z_1 + z_2) + z_3$
$= z_1 + (z_2 + z_3)$.

A5. If $z_1, z_2 \in \mathbb{C}$, then
$z_1 + z_2 = z_2 + z_1$.

Multiplication

M1. If $z_1, z_2 \in \mathbb{C}$, then
$z_1 \times z_2 \in \mathbb{C}$.

M2. If $z \in \mathbb{C}$, then
$z \times 1 = 1 \times z = z$.

M3. If $z \in \mathbb{C} - \{0\}$, then
there is a number
$z^{-1} \in \mathbb{C}$ such that
$z \times z^{-1} = z^{-1} \times z = 1$.

M4. If $z_1, z_2, z_3 \in \mathbb{C}$, then
$(z_1 \times z_2) \times z_3$
$= z_1 \times (z_2 \times z_3)$.

M5. If $z_1, z_2 \in \mathbb{C}$, then
$z_1 \times z_2 = z_2 \times z_1$.

CLOSURE

IDENTITY

INVERSES

ASSOCIATIVITY

COMMUTATIVITY

D. If $z_1, z_2, z_3 \in \mathbb{C}$, then $z_1 \times (z_2 + z_3) = z_1 \times z_2 + z_1 \times z_3$.

DISTRIBUTIVITY

In particular, $0 = 0 + 0i$ plays the same role in $\mathbb{C}$ as the real number 0 does in $\mathbb{R}$, and $1 = 1 + 0i$ plays the same role as 1. These numbers are called *identities* for addition and multiplication respectively.

We also have that the *additive inverse* (or negative) of $z = x + yi$ is $-z = -x - yi$, and the *multiplicative inverse* (or reciprocal) of $z = x + yi$ is

$$\frac{\overline{z}}{|z|^2} = \frac{x - yi}{x^2 + y^2}, \quad \text{for } z \neq 0.$$

There is one important difference between the set of real numbers and the set of complex numbers, however; namely that, unlike the real numbers, the complex numbers are not ordered.

For any two real numbers a and b, exactly one of the three properties

$$a < b, \quad a = b \quad \text{or} \quad a > b$$

is true. But this is not the case for the complex numbers; we cannot say, for example, that

$$1 + 2i > -1 + 3i \quad \text{or} \quad 1 + 2i = -1 + 3i \quad \text{or} \quad 1 + 2i < -1 + 3i.$$

Inequalities involving complex numbers make sense only if they are inequalities between real quantities, such as the moduli of the complex numbers. For example, inequalities such as

Moduli is the plural of modulus.

$$|z - 2i| \leq 3 \quad \text{or} \quad \operatorname{Re} z > 5$$

are valid.

2.2 Polar form

You have seen that the complex number $x + iy$ corresponds to the point (x, y) in the complex plane. This correspondence enables us to give an alternative description of complex numbers, using so-called *polar form*. This form is particularly useful when we discuss properties related to multiplication and division of complex numbers.

Polar form is obtained by noting that the point in the complex plane associated with the non-zero complex number $z = x + iy$ is uniquely determined by the modulus $r = |z| = \sqrt{x^2 + y^2}$, together with the angle θ (measured in an anticlockwise direction in radians) between the positive direction of the x-axis and the line from the origin to the point, as shown in the margin. We have

$$x = r \cos \theta \quad \text{and} \quad y = r \sin \theta,$$

so the complex number z can be expressed as

$$z = r(\cos \theta + i \sin \theta).$$

This description of z in terms of r and θ is not unique because the angle θ is determined only up to multiples of 2π; that is, the angles $\theta \pm 2\pi$, $\theta \pm 4\pi$, $\theta \pm 6\pi$, ..., also determine the same complex number. However, if we restrict the angle θ to lie in the interval $(-\pi, \pi]$, then the description *is* unique. The origin is an exception, however: at the origin the value of r is 0, and θ is not defined.

Some texts restrict θ to lie in the interval $[0, 2\pi)$.

Definitions   A non-zero complex number $z = x + iy$ is in **polar form** if it is expressed as

$$r(\cos\theta + i\sin\theta),$$

where $r = |z|$ and θ is any angle (measured in radians anticlockwise) between the positive direction of the x-axis and the line joining z to the origin.

Such an angle θ is called an **argument** of the complex number z, and is denoted by $\arg z$. The **principal argument** of z is the value of $\arg z$ that lies in the interval $(-\pi, \pi]$, and is denoted by $\operatorname{Arg} z$.

Some texts use $r\operatorname{cis}\theta$ or $\langle r, \theta\rangle$ as shorthand for $r(\cos\theta + i\sin\theta)$.

Here *principal argument* is a shortened form of the more conventional 'principal *value of the* argument'.

Remark   Sometimes we refer to $z = x + iy$ as the *Cartesian form* of z, to distinguish it from polar form.

We now discuss how to convert a complex number from polar form to Cartesian form, and vice versa.

When carrying out such conversions, it is useful to remember the values in the table below, as these will help you in some special cases. You may find it easier to remember the triangles, from which you can work out most of the values in the table.

θ	0	$\pi/6$	$\pi/4$	$\pi/3$	$\pi/2$
$\sin\theta$	0	$\frac{1}{2}$	$\frac{1}{\sqrt{2}}$	$\frac{\sqrt{3}}{2}$	1
$\cos\theta$	1	$\frac{\sqrt{3}}{2}$	$\frac{1}{\sqrt{2}}$	$\frac{1}{2}$	0

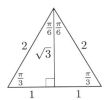 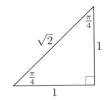

The following formulas are also helpful. For any $\theta \in \mathbb{R}$:

$$\sin(\pi - \theta) = \sin\theta, \qquad \sin(-\theta) = -\sin\theta, \quad \sin(\pi + \theta) = -\sin\theta;$$
$$\cos(\pi - \theta) = -\cos\theta, \quad \cos(-\theta) = \cos\theta, \qquad \cos(\pi + \theta) = -\cos\theta.$$

You will need only the first two equations in each row; the other equations are given for completeness.

You may be able to remember these formulas by roughly sketching graphs of the sine and cosine functions, and using their symmetry. For example, we can sketch the sine function as follows.

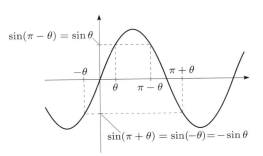

To convert a complex number from polar form to Cartesian form is straightforward: we use the equations

$$x = r\cos\theta, \quad y = r\sin\theta$$

to find x and y given r and θ. This is illustrated in the following example.

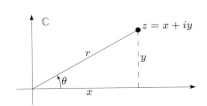

Example 2.3   Express each of the following complex numbers in Cartesian form.

(a) $3(\cos(\pi/3) + i\sin(\pi/3))$ (b) $\cos(-\pi/6) + i\sin(-\pi/6)$

Solution

(a) Here $r = 3$ and $\theta = \pi/3$. Thus the required form is $x + iy$, where

$$x = 3\cos(\pi/3) = 3 \times \tfrac{1}{2} = \tfrac{3}{2}$$

and

$$y = 3\sin(\pi/3) = 3 \times \tfrac{1}{2}\sqrt{3} = \tfrac{3}{2}\sqrt{3}.$$

The Cartesian form is therefore $\tfrac{3}{2} + \tfrac{3}{2}\sqrt{3}i$.

(b) Here $r = 1$ and $\theta = -\pi/6$. Thus the required form is $x + iy$, where

$$x = \cos(-\pi/6) = \cos(\pi/6) = \tfrac{1}{2}\sqrt{3}$$

and

$$y = \sin(-\pi/6) = -\sin(\pi/6) = -\tfrac{1}{2}.$$

The Cartesian form is therefore $\tfrac{1}{2}\sqrt{3} - \tfrac{1}{2}i$. ∎

Exercise 2.10 Express each of the following complex numbers in Cartesian form.

(a) $2(\cos(\pi/2) + i\sin(\pi/2))$ (b) $4(\cos(-2\pi/3) + i\sin(-2\pi/3))$

To convert a non-zero complex number z from Cartesian form $x + iy$ to polar form $r(\cos\theta + i\sin\theta)$, we first find the modulus r using the formula

$$r = \sqrt{x^2 + y^2}.$$

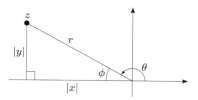

If z is either real or imaginary, then it lies on one of the axes and has principal argument 0, $\pi/2$, π or $-\pi/2$, as shown in diagram (a) below. Otherwise, to find the principal argument θ, we need to solve the equations

$$\cos\theta = \frac{x}{r} \quad \text{and} \quad \sin\theta = \frac{y}{r}, \quad \text{where } \theta \in (-\pi, \pi].$$

We can do this by first finding the first-quadrant angle ϕ that satisfies the related equation

$$\cos\phi = \frac{|x|}{r} \quad \left(\text{or, equivalently, } \sin\phi = \frac{|y|}{r} \text{ or } \tan\phi = \left|\frac{y}{x}\right|\right).$$

ϕ is the angle at the origin in the right-angled triangle formed by drawing the perpendicular from z to the real axis, as illustrated above in the case where z lies in the second quadrant. We have

$$\cos\phi = \frac{|x|}{r}$$

and the relationship between θ and ϕ can be seen to be as given in diagram (b).

The relationship of ϕ to the principal argument θ depends on the quadrant in which z lies, as indicated in diagram (b) below.

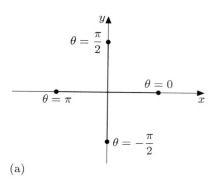

(a)

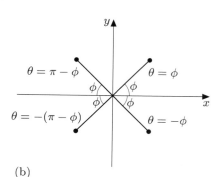

(b)

The quadrant in which z lies can be found from the values of x and y, and θ can then be deduced by using the appropriate equation from diagram (b).

You may find it helpful to sketch z on an Argand diagram.

This method for finding θ is used in the next example, which illustrates how the Cartesian form of a complex number is converted into polar form.

Example 2.4   Express each of the following complex numbers in polar form, using the principal argument.

(a) $2 + 2i$ (b) $-\frac{1}{2} - \frac{1}{2}\sqrt{3}i$

Solution

(a) Let $z = x + iy = 2 + 2i$, so $x = 2$ and $y = 2$.

Then $z = r(\cos\theta + i\sin\theta)$, where

$$r = \sqrt{x^2 + y^2} = \sqrt{2^2 + 2^2} = \sqrt{8} = 2\sqrt{2}.$$

To find θ, we calculate

$$\cos\phi = \frac{|x|}{r} = \frac{2}{2\sqrt{2}} = \frac{1}{\sqrt{2}}.$$

So $\phi = \pi/4$, and z lies in the first quadrant so $\theta = \phi = \pi/4$.

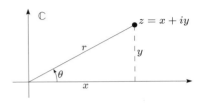

The polar form of $2 + 2i$ in terms of the principal argument is therefore

$$2\sqrt{2}(\cos(\pi/4) + i\sin(\pi/4)).$$

(b) Let $z = x + iy = -\frac{1}{2} - \frac{1}{2}\sqrt{3}i$, so $x = -\frac{1}{2}$ and $y = -\frac{1}{2}\sqrt{3}$.

Then $z = r(\cos\theta + i\sin\theta)$, where

$$r = \sqrt{x^2 + y^2} = \sqrt{(-\tfrac{1}{2})^2 + (-\tfrac{1}{2}\sqrt{3})^2} = 1.$$

To find θ, we calculate

$$\cos\phi = \frac{|x|}{r} = \frac{|-\frac{1}{2}|}{1} = \frac{1}{2}.$$

So $\phi = \pi/3$, and z lies in the third quadrant so $\theta = -(\pi - \phi) = -2\pi/3$.

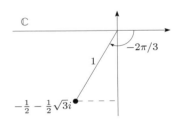

The polar form of $-\frac{1}{2} - \frac{1}{2}\sqrt{3}i$ in terms of the principal argument is therefore

$$\cos(-2\pi/3) + i\sin(-2\pi/3). \quad \blacksquare$$

Exercise 2.11   Draw a diagram showing each of the following complex numbers in the complex plane, and express them in polar form, using the principal argument.

(a) $-1 + i$ (b) $1 - \sqrt{3}i$ (c) -5

Polar form gives us a simple way to multiply complex numbers. Let

$$z_1 = r_1(\cos\theta_1 + i\sin\theta_1) \quad \text{and} \quad z_2 = r_2(\cos\theta_2 + i\sin\theta_2);$$

then

$$\begin{aligned}
z_1 z_2 &= r_1(\cos\theta_1 + i\sin\theta_1) \times r_2(\cos\theta_2 + i\sin\theta_2) \\
&= r_1 r_2(\cos\theta_1 + i\sin\theta_1)(\cos\theta_2 + i\sin\theta_2) \\
&= r_1 r_2(\cos\theta_1\cos\theta_2 + i\sin\theta_1\cos\theta_2 + i\cos\theta_1\sin\theta_2 + i^2\sin\theta_1\sin\theta_2) \\
&= r_1 r_2((\cos\theta_1\cos\theta_2 - \sin\theta_1\sin\theta_2) + i(\sin\theta_1\cos\theta_2 + \cos\theta_1\sin\theta_2)) \\
&= r_1 r_2(\cos(\theta_1 + \theta_2) + i\sin(\theta_1 + \theta_2)).
\end{aligned}$$

Here we use the addition formulas for the trigonometric functions, given in Unit I1, Section 4.

That is, to multiply two complex numbers in polar form, we multiply their moduli and add their arguments. For example,

$$\begin{aligned}
&2(\cos\tfrac{1}{4}\pi + i\sin\tfrac{1}{4}\pi) \times 3(\cos\tfrac{1}{3}\pi + i\sin\tfrac{1}{3}\pi) \\
&= 6(\cos\tfrac{7}{12}\pi + i\sin\tfrac{7}{12}\pi).
\end{aligned}$$
(2.1)

$2 \times 3 = 6$ and $\frac{1}{4}\pi + \frac{1}{3}\pi = \frac{7}{12}\pi$. In the rest of this section we usually write $\pi/4$ as $\frac{1}{4}\pi$, and similarly for other fractions of π. You may use either form, or the form $\dfrac{\pi}{4}$, as you wish.

We can also use formula (2.1) for the product of two complex numbers in polar form to establish a similar formula for the *quotient* of two complex numbers. Specifically, we show that if

$$z_1 = r_1(\cos\theta_1 + i\sin\theta_1) \quad \text{and} \quad z_2 = r_2(\cos\theta_2 + i\sin\theta_2),$$

with $z_2 \neq 0$, then z_1/z_2 is the complex number

$$z = r(\cos\theta + i\sin\theta), \text{ where } r = r_1/r_2 \text{ and } \theta = \theta_1 - \theta_2. \qquad\qquad z_2 \neq 0 \Rightarrow r_2 \neq 0$$

To see this, notice that since $r_1 = rr_2$ and $\theta_1 = \theta + \theta_2$ it follows from the above discussion that $z_1 = zz_2$. Hence $z_1/z_2 = z$, as required. We can write the formula as

$$\frac{z_1}{z_2} = \frac{r_1}{r_2}(\cos(\theta_1 - \theta_2) + i\sin(\theta_1 - \theta_2)), \quad \text{provided that } z_2 \neq 0. \qquad (2.2)$$

That is, to divide a complex number z_1 by another complex number z_2, we divide the modulus of z_1 by the modulus of z_2, and subtract the argument of z_2 from the argument of z_1.

For example,

$$\frac{2\left(\cos\frac{1}{4}\pi + i\sin\frac{1}{4}\pi\right)}{3\left(\cos\frac{1}{3}\pi + i\sin\frac{1}{3}\pi\right)} = \frac{2}{3}\cos\left(-\frac{1}{12}\pi\right) + i\sin(-\frac{1}{12}\pi). \qquad\qquad 2 \div 3 = \frac{2}{3} \text{ and } \frac{1}{4}\pi - \frac{1}{3}\pi = -\frac{1}{12}\pi.$$

In particular, if $z = r(\cos\theta + i\sin\theta)$ with $r \neq 0$, then the reciprocal of z is

$$\frac{1}{z} = \frac{1}{r}(\cos(-\theta) + i\sin(-\theta)). \qquad (2.3)$$

The above methods for multiplying and dividing complex numbers in polar form are summarised below.

Strategy 2.1

To multiply two complex numbers given in polar form, multiply their moduli and add their arguments.

To divide a complex number z_1 by a non-zero complex number z_2 when both are given in polar form, divide the modulus of z_1 by the modulus of z_2, and subtract the argument of z_2 from the argument of z_1.

Remark If you require the *principal* argument of the product or quotient, then you may need to add or subtract 2π from the argument calculated.

Exercise 2.12 Determine each of the following products and quotients in polar form in terms of the principal argument.

(a) $4\left(\cos(-\frac{1}{6}\pi) + i\sin(-\frac{1}{6}\pi)\right) \times \frac{1}{2}\left(\cos(\frac{7}{8}\pi) + i\sin(\frac{7}{8}\pi)\right)$

(b) $3\left(\cos(\frac{2}{3}\pi) + i\sin(\frac{2}{3}\pi)\right) \times \frac{1}{2}\left(\cos(\frac{1}{2}\pi) + i\sin(\frac{1}{2}\pi)\right)$

(c) $\dfrac{4\left(\cos(-\frac{1}{6}\pi) + i\sin(-\frac{1}{6}\pi)\right)}{\frac{1}{2}\left(\cos(\frac{7}{8}\pi) + i\sin(\frac{7}{8}\pi)\right)}$

(d) $\dfrac{3\left(\cos(\frac{2}{3}\pi) + i\sin(\frac{2}{3}\pi)\right)}{\frac{1}{2}\left(\cos(\frac{1}{2}\pi) + i\sin(\frac{1}{2}\pi)\right)}$

2.3 Roots of polynomials

We begin by reminding you of what we mean by the word 'root'. In this unit we use this term in two different, but related, senses, as given below.

Definition   If $p(z)$ is a polynomial, then the solutions of the polynomial equation $p(z) = 0$ are called the **roots** of $p(z)$.

If a is a complex number, then the solutions of the equation $z^n = a$ are called the nth **roots** of a.

The roots of a polynomial are also called its *zeros*.

Thus the nth roots of a are the roots of the polynomial $z^n - a$.

In this subsection we explain how to find the nth roots of any complex number and we discuss the roots of polynomial equations more generally.

The formula obtained in the previous section for finding the product of two complex numbers in polar form can be generalised to a product of several complex numbers.

Strategy 2.2

To find the product of the complex numbers $z_1, z_2, \ldots, z_n$ given in polar form, multiply their moduli and add their arguments.

Exercise 2.13   Let $z_1 = -1 + i$, $z_2 = 1 - \sqrt{3}i$ and $z_3 = -5$. Use the solution to Exercise 2.11 to express $z_1 z_2 z_3$ and $\dfrac{z_2 z_3}{z_1}$ in polar form.

An important special case of the result in Strategy 2.2 is obtained when $z_1 = z_2 = \ldots = z_n = r(\cos\theta + i\sin\theta)$; that is, when the complex numbers $z_1, z_2, \ldots, z_n$ are all equal. In this case, the result gives

$$(r(\cos\theta + i\sin\theta))^n = r^n(\cos n\theta + i\sin n\theta); \quad n = 1, 2, \ldots. \tag{2.4}$$

$n\theta$ may not be the *principal* argument of $(\cos\theta + i\sin\theta)^n$.

Example 2.5   Find z^4, where $z = 1 + i$.

Solution $1 + i = \sqrt{2}(\cos(\tfrac{1}{4}\pi) + i\sin(\tfrac{1}{4}\pi))$, so

$$(1 + i)^4 = (\sqrt{2})^4(\cos(4 \times \tfrac{1}{4}\pi) + i\sin(4 \times \tfrac{1}{4}\pi))$$
$$= 4(\cos\pi + i\sin\pi) = -4.$$

So $z^4 = -4$.   ■

The significant new information obtained from equation (2.4) is that

$$(\cos\theta + i\sin\theta)^n = \cos n\theta + i\sin n\theta, \quad \text{for all } n \in \mathbb{N}.$$

This result is true for all $n \in \mathbb{Z}$ and is known as *de Moivre's Theorem.*

Abraham de Moivre was a French mathematician who worked in England from 1685 after the expulsion of the Huguenots from France.

Theorem 2.1 de Moivre's Theorem

If $z = \cos\theta + i\sin\theta$, then, for any $n \in \mathbb{Z}$,

$$z^n = (\cos\theta + i\sin\theta)^n = \cos n\theta + i\sin n\theta.$$

We have seen that de Moivre's Theorem is true when n is a positive integer. We now show that it is true for other integers.

For $n = 0$,

$$(\cos\theta + i\sin\theta)^0 = 1 = \cos(0 \times \theta) + i\sin(0 \times \theta).$$

For $n = -m$, where m is a positive integer,

$$
\begin{aligned}
(\cos\theta + i\sin\theta)^n &= (\cos\theta + i\sin\theta)^{-m} \\
&= \frac{1}{(\cos\theta + i\sin\theta)^m} \\
&= \frac{1}{\cos(m\theta) + i\sin(m\theta)} \\
&= \cos(-m\theta) + i\sin(-m\theta) \\
&= \cos n\theta + i\sin n\theta.
\end{aligned}
$$

Here we use formula (2.3).

One application of de Moivre's Theorem is in finding the nth roots of complex numbers; that is, in solving equations of the form $z^n = a$, where $a \in \mathbb{C}$. Before we illustrate this, we use the theorem to verify some solutions of such an equation.

Exercise 2.14

(a) Express the complex number 1 in polar form.

(b) Show that each of the three complex numbers with polar forms $1(\cos 0 + i\sin 0)$, $1\left(\cos(\tfrac{2}{3}\pi) + i\sin(\tfrac{2}{3}\pi)\right)$ and $1\left(\cos(\tfrac{4}{3}\pi) + i\sin(\tfrac{4}{3}\pi)\right)$ satisfies the equation $z^3 = 1$.

(c) Express in Cartesian form the three solutions to the equation $z^3 = 1$ given in part (b).

The solution to Exercise 2.14 verifies that the three given complex numbers are solutions of the equation $z^3 = 1$. However, what we really want is a method which will enable us to find solutions of such an equation without knowing them in advance. Fortunately, de Moivre's Theorem enables us to do this.

Example 2.6

(a) Express the equation $z^3 = -27$ in polar form.

(b) Find three different solutions of the equation $z^3 = -27$, by using the fact that adding any multiple of 2π to an argument of -27 gives another argument of -27.

Solution

(a) In polar form, $-27 = 27(\cos\pi + i\sin\pi)$. If $z = r(\cos\theta + i\sin\theta)$, then the equation $z^3 = -27$ can be written as

$$
r^3(\cos 3\theta + i\sin 3\theta) = 27(\cos\pi + i\sin\pi). \tag{2.5}
$$

(b) From equation (2.5), $r^3 = 27$, so $r = 3$.

Also from equation (2.5), $\cos 3\theta = \cos\pi$ and $\sin 3\theta = \sin\pi$, so one solution for θ is obtained by taking $3\theta = \pi$, so $\theta = \tfrac{1}{3}\pi$.

However, we could also take 3π, 5π, 7π, ... as arguments of -27, so $3\theta = 3\pi$, $3\theta = 5\pi$, $3\theta = 7\pi$, ... also give solutions. Hence we can have $\theta = \tfrac{1}{3}\pi$, $\theta = \pi$, $\theta = \tfrac{5}{3}\pi$, $\theta = \tfrac{7}{3}\pi$, ...

But $\tfrac{7}{3}\pi = 2\pi + \tfrac{1}{3}\pi$, so taking $\theta = \tfrac{7}{3}\pi$ gives the same complex number as $\theta = \tfrac{1}{3}\pi$.

Similarly, increasing the value of the argument of -27 by any further multiple of 2π repeats solutions we already have.

So the three different solutions of $z^3 = -27$ are given by

$$z_1 = 3\left(\cos(\tfrac{1}{3}\pi) + i\sin(\tfrac{1}{3}\pi)\right),$$
$$z_2 = 3(\cos\pi + i\sin\pi),$$
$$z_3 = 3\left(\cos(\tfrac{5}{3}\pi) + i\sin(\tfrac{5}{3}\pi)\right).$$

These solutions can also be written in Cartesian form as

$$z_1 = \frac{3}{2} + i\frac{3\sqrt{3}}{2}, \quad z_2 = -3, \quad z_3 = \frac{3}{2} - i\frac{3\sqrt{3}}{2}.$$

They are shown in the diagram. ■

The solution z_3 could be rewritten in terms of its principal argument as $3(\cos(-\pi/3) + i\sin(-\pi/3))$.

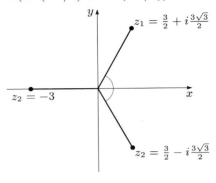

Now we show how we can use the method of Example 2.6 to find the solutions of any complex equation of the form

$$z^n = a,$$

where a is a known complex number. We write both z and a in polar form so that, say,

$$z = r(\cos\theta + i\sin\theta) \quad \text{and} \quad a = \rho(\cos\phi + i\sin\phi),$$

where r and θ are variables whose values we must find, and ρ and ϕ are known real numbers.

Then $z^n = a$ gives, using de Moivre's Theorem,

$$r^n(\cos n\theta + i\sin n\theta) = \rho(\cos\phi + i\sin\phi).$$

Hence we must have $r^n = \rho$, so $r = \rho^{1/n}$. Also $n\theta$ must represent the same angle as ϕ. Now we use the fact that a complex number has many arguments. Since adding on any multiple of 2π to the argument ϕ of a gives the same complex number a, we can have

$$n\theta = \phi + 2k\pi, \quad \text{for any integer } k,$$

that is,

$$\theta = \frac{\phi}{n} + \frac{2k\pi}{n}, \quad \text{for any integer } k.$$

If $k = n$ we have $\theta = \phi/n + 2\pi$, which is the same angle as ϕ/n. So taking $k = 0, 1, 2, \ldots, n-1$ will give the n different solutions of the equation $z^n = a$. We thus arrive at the following conclusion.

Roots of a complex number Let $a = \rho(\cos\phi + i\sin\phi)$ be a complex number in polar form. Then, for any $n \in \mathbb{N}$, the equation $z^n = a$ has n solutions, given by

$$z = \rho^{1/n}\left(\cos\left(\frac{\phi}{n} + \frac{2k\pi}{n}\right) + i\sin\left(\frac{\phi}{n} + \frac{2k\pi}{n}\right)\right),$$

for $k = 0, 1, \ldots, n-1$.

Exercise 2.15

(a) Express the equation $z^6 = 1$ in polar form.

(b) Use the method described above to find the six solutions of $z^6 = 1$ in polar form.

(c) Sketch the position of each solution in the complex plane.

(d) Find the Cartesian form of each solution.

In Exercise 2.15 you found the solutions of the equation $z^6 = 1$. These are known as the sixth roots of unity, and in the complex plane they are equally spaced around the circle of radius 1, centre the origin. More generally, the solutions of the equation $z^n = 1$ are known as the **nth roots of unity** and in the complex plane they are equally spaced around the circle of radius 1, centre the origin. For any $n \in \mathbb{N}$, one of the nth roots of unity is 1.

The nth roots of any complex number are equally spaced around a circle with centre the origin, but the circle may not have radius 1 and there may not be a root on the real axis.

Exercise 2.16   Solve the equation $z^4 = -4$, expressing your answers in Cartesian form. Mark your solutions on a diagram of the complex plane.

Exercise 2.17   Solve the equation $z^3 = 8i$, expressing your answers in Cartesian form. Mark your solutions on a diagram of the complex plane.

The result in the box above gives the n solutions of any equation of the form $z^n = a$, where a is a non-zero complex number. Now the equation $z^n = a$, which can be written as $z^n - a = 0$, is an example of a polynomial equation whose coefficients are complex numbers. Other examples of polynomial equations with complex coefficients are

$$z^2 + i = 0$$

and

$$(1 + i)z^5 + 2iz^3 - 3z^2 + (1 - 2i)z - 1 = 0.$$

Remarkably, it can be shown that *any* polynomial equation

$$a_n z^n + a_{n-1} z^{n-1} + \cdots + a_1 z + a_0 = 0,$$

where $a_n, a_{n-1}, \ldots, a_0 \in \mathbb{C}$ and $a_n \neq 0$, has at least one solution in $\mathbb{C}$. Moreover, it cannot have more than n solutions.

The complex numbers are, unlike the reals, an 'algebraically closed' system of numbers. By this we mean that any polynomial equation with coefficients in $\mathbb{C}$ has a solution in $\mathbb{C}$. The fact that any polynomial equation with complex coefficients necessarily has a complex solution is called the *Fundamental Theorem of Algebra*. We do not prove this theorem in this course.

It is often not easy to find such solutions! However, in some cases we can combine the methods of the Polynomial Factorisation Theorem below and the use of de Moivre's Theorem to find solutions of a polynomial equation.

You met the Polynomial Factorisation Theorem for real roots of a polynomial in Unit I2. The theorem is also true in $\mathbb{C}$.

If we count coincident solutions separately so that, for example, in the equation

$$(z - 1)^3 (z + 4)^2 (z - 5) = 0$$

the solution 1 is counted three times, the solution -4 is counted twice and the solution 5 is counted once, then a polynomial equation of degree n has *exactly* n solutions.

Theorem 2.2 Polynomial Factorisation Theorem

Let $p(z)$ be a polynomial of degree n with coefficients in $\mathbb{C}$ and let $\alpha \in \mathbb{C}$. Then $p(\alpha) = 0$ if and only if

$$p(z) = (z - \alpha)q(z),$$

where $q(z)$ is a polynomial of degree $n - 1$ with coefficients in $\mathbb{C}$.

In this statement of the theorem, we have used z in place of x, as this is the label usually used for a complex variable. The proof is otherwise exactly the same as the proof for the theorem in $\mathbb{R}$, so we do not include it here.

From the Fundamental Theorem of Algebra, mathematical induction and the Polynomial Factorisation Theorem, we can deduce the following important corollary.

Corollary

Every polynomial $p(z) = a_n z^n + a_{n-1} z^{n-1} + \cdots + a_1 z + a_0$, where $n \geq 1$, $a_i \in \mathbb{C}$ for each i and $a_n \neq 0$, has a factorisation

$$p(z) = a_n(z - \alpha_1)(z - \alpha_2) \cdots (z - \alpha_n),$$

where the complex numbers $\alpha_1, \alpha_2, \ldots, \alpha_n$ are the roots (not necessarily distinct) of $p(z)$.

Proof   Let $S(n)$ be the statement of the corollary for general $n \geq 1$.

Then $S(1)$ is true, since the polynomial

$$p(z) = a_1 z + a_0 \qquad 0 = a_1 z + a_0 \qquad z = \frac{-a_0}{a_1}$$

(where $a_1 \neq 0$) has the root $\alpha_1 = -a_0/a_1$ and has a factorisation

$$p(z) = a_1(z - \alpha_1).$$

Now suppose that $S(k)$ is true, and consider any polynomial of degree $k + 1$:

$$p(z) = a_{k+1} z^{k+1} + a_k z^k + \cdots + a_1 z + a_0,$$

where $a_{k+1} \neq 0$. By the Fundamental Theorem of Algebra, the equation $p(z) = 0$ has at least one solution, say α_{k+1}, in $\mathbb{C}$. Then, by the Polynomial Factorisation Theorem,

$$p(z) = (z - \alpha_{k+1})q(z),$$

where $q(z)$ is a polynomial of degree k. Now the coefficient of z^k in $q(z)$ must be a_{k+1}. Thus, by $S(k)$, this polynomial has a factorisation

$$q(z) = a_{k+1}(z - \alpha_1)(z - \alpha_2) \cdots (z - \alpha_k).$$

Thus

$$\begin{aligned} p(z) &= (z - \alpha_{k+1})a_{k+1}(z - \alpha_1)(z - \alpha_2) \cdots (z - \alpha_k) \\ &= a_{k+1}(z - \alpha_1)(z - \alpha_2) \cdots (z - \alpha_k)(z - \alpha_{k+1}). \end{aligned}$$

Therefore $S(k)$ true $\Rightarrow S(k + 1)$ true, so by mathematical induction $S(n)$ is true for every positive integer n.   ∎

You may have noticed that it follows from the quadratic formula (see page 7) that, for a quadratic equation with *real* coefficients, the roots are either both real or occur as a complex conjugate pair.

This holds for polynomial equations in general; if $p(z)$ is a polynomial in z with real coefficients, then whenever α is a root of p, so is $\overline{\alpha}$. Moreover, the factors $z - \alpha$ and $z - \overline{\alpha}$ can be combined to give a real quadratic factor of $p(z)$, namely

$$(z - \alpha)(z - \overline{\alpha}) = z^2 - (\alpha + \overline{\alpha})z + \alpha\overline{\alpha},$$

which has real coefficients, since $\alpha + \overline{\alpha} = 2\operatorname{Re}\alpha$ and $\alpha\overline{\alpha} = |\alpha|^2$.

$S(n)$ is the statement in the box above. We use the notation $S(n)$ instead of the more usual $P(n)$ to avoid confusion with the polynomial $p(z)$.

We omit the proof of this result.

25

Example 2.7

(a) Show that $z = i$ is a root of the polynomial
$$p(z) = z^4 - 3z^3 + 2z^2 - 3z + 1.$$

(b) Hence find all the roots of $p(z)$.

Solution

(a) $p(i) = i^4 - 3i^3 + 2i^2 - 3i + 1$
$= 1 + 3i - 2 - 3i + 1 = 0,$

so i is a root of $p(z)$.

(b) Since p has real coefficients, $z = -i$ is also a root of $p(z)$, so $(z - i)(z + i) = z^2 + 1$ is a factor of $p(z)$. By equating coefficients, we obtain
$$z^4 - 3z^3 + 2z^2 - 3z + 1 = (z^2 + 1)(z^2 - 3z + 1).$$

So the remaining two roots of $p(z)$ are given by the solutions of the equation $z^2 - 3z + 1 = 0$.

Using the quadratic formula, we have
$$z = \frac{3 \pm \sqrt{9 - 4}}{2} = \frac{3 \pm \sqrt{5}}{2}.$$

Hence the four roots of $p(z)$ are i, $-i$, $\dfrac{3 + \sqrt{5}}{2}$ and $\dfrac{3 - \sqrt{5}}{2}$. ∎

Exercise 2.18   Find, in the form $a_n z^n + \cdots + a_1 z + a_0$, a polynomial whose roots are 1, -2, $3i$ and $-3i$.

Earlier in this subsection we used de Moivre's Theorem to find roots of complex numbers. Another use of de Moivre's Theorem is to find further trigonometric identities similar to those given in Unit I1.   See Unit I1, Section 4.

Exercise 2.19   Using de Moivre's Theorem, we have
$$(\cos\theta + i\sin\theta)^3 = \cos 3\theta + i\sin 3\theta,$$

for all $\theta \in \mathbb{R}$.

(a) Expand the left-hand side of the above expression using the Binomial Theorem. Then express your answer in the form $x + iy$,   See Unit I2, Theorem 4.1. where x and y are expressions involving $\cos\theta$ and $\sin\theta$.

(b) By equating real and imaginary parts, use your answer to part (a) to obtain formulas for $\cos 3\theta$ and $\sin 3\theta$ in terms of $\cos\theta$ and $\sin\theta$.

(c) Use your answer to part (b) and the identity $\cos^2\theta + \sin^2\theta = 1$ to obtain a formula for $\cos 3\theta$ in terms of $\cos\theta$ and a formula for $\sin 3\theta$ in terms of $\sin\theta$.

The method of Solution 2.19 generalises to produce formulas for $\cos n\theta$ and $\sin n\theta$ for all $n \in \mathbb{N}$.

Exercise 2.20

(a) Use de Moivre's Theorem to obtain formulas for $\cos 5\theta$ and $\sin 5\theta$ in terms of $\cos\theta$ and $\sin\theta$.

(b) Use your answer to part (a) and the identity $\cos^2\theta + \sin^2\theta = 1$ to find a formula for $\cos 5\theta$ in terms of $\cos\theta$ and a formula for $\sin 5\theta$ in terms of $\sin\theta$.

2.4 The complex exponential function

In Unit I1 we considered the real exponential function $f(x) = e^x$ (that is, $f(x) = \exp x$). We now extend the definition of this function to define a function $f(z) = e^z$ whose domain and codomain are $\mathbb{C}$.

We expect complex powers of e to satisfy the familiar properties of real powers of e. For example, we expect that

$$e^{z_1}e^{z_2} = e^{z_1+z_2}, \quad \text{for all } z_1, z_2 \in \mathbb{C}.$$

If this is to be achieved, then the definition of e^z has to be as follows.

Definition   If $z = x + iy$, then $e^z = e^x e^{iy} = e^x(\cos y + i \sin y)$.

We consider the real function $f(x) = e^x$ in more detail in the analysis units.

This definition of e^z is discussed in more detail in courses on complex analysis.

Example 2.8   Show that

$$e^{z_1}e^{z_2} = e^{z_1+z_2}$$

for all complex numbers z_1 and z_2.

Solution   We use Strategy 2.1.

Suppose that $z_1 = x_1 + iy_1$ and $z_2 = x_2 + iy_2$. Then

$$\begin{aligned}
e^{z_1}e^{z_2} &= e^{x_1}(\cos y_1 + i \sin y_1)e^{x_2}(\cos y_2 + i \sin y_2) \\
&= e^{x_1}e^{x_2}(\cos y_1 + i \sin y_1)(\cos y_2 + i \sin y_2) \\
&= e^{x_1+x_2}(\cos(y_1+y_2) + i \sin(y_1+y_2)) \\
&= e^{(x_1+x_2)+i(y_1+y_2)} \\
&= e^{(x_1+i_1 y)+(x_2+i_2 y)} \\
&= e^{z_1+z_2}. \quad \blacksquare
\end{aligned}$$

See page 20.

We assume that if x_1, x_2 are *real* numbers, then
$$e^{x_1}e^{x_2} = e^{x_1+x_2}.$$
This rule is discussed in the analysis units.

Exercise 2.21

(a) Using the above definition for e^z and de Moivre's Theorem, show that

$$\frac{1}{e^z} = e^{-z}, \quad \text{for all } z \in \mathbb{C}.$$

(b) Show that $e^{z_1}/e^{z_2} = e^{z_1-z_2}$, for all $z_1, z_2 \in \mathbb{C}$.

So the rules for multiplication and division of complex powers of e are exactly the same as those for real powers. Furthermore, when the exponent z is real, that is when $z = x + 0i$, where $x \in \mathbb{R}$, the definitions of a real and a complex power of e coincide, since

$$e^z = e^{x+i0} = e^x(\cos 0 + i \sin 0) = e^x.$$

On the other hand, if $z = 0 + iy$, where $y \in \mathbb{R}$, then the definition gives

$$e^{iy} = \cos y + i \sin y.$$

This is known as **Euler's formula**. Putting $y = \pi$, we obtain

$$e^{i\pi} = e^0(\cos \pi + i \sin \pi) = 1(-1 + i0) = -1,$$

or

$$e^{i\pi} + 1 = 0.$$

This is a remarkable relationship between five important numbers: 0, 1, i, π and e.

The formula $e^{iy} = \cos y + i \sin y$ gives us an alternative form for the expression of a complex number in polar form. If

$$z = x + iy = r(\cos\theta + i\sin\theta),$$

then we can write $\cos\theta + i\sin\theta$ as $e^{i\theta}$, so

$$z = re^{i\theta}.$$

A complex number expressed in this way is said to be in **exponential form**. Using this notation, de Moivre's Theorem becomes the simple result

$$(e^{i\theta})^n = e^{in\theta}, \quad \text{for all } \theta \in \mathbb{R} \text{ and all } n \in \mathbb{Z}.$$

Some texts refer to $re^{i\theta}$ as *polar form*.

We can use the complex exponential function to find some further useful trigonometric identities. At the end of Section 2.3 we showed how de Moivre's Theorem can be used to express the sine or cosine of a multiple of θ in terms of powers of $\sin\theta$ and $\cos\theta$. Here we do the opposite, expressing a power of $\sin\theta$ or $\cos\theta$ as a combination of sines or cosines of multiples of θ.

First, we deduce two useful equations. We know that, for all $\theta \in \mathbb{R}$,

$$\cos\theta + i\sin\theta = e^{i\theta}. \tag{2.6}$$

Also, since $\cos(-\theta) + i\sin(-\theta) = \cos\theta - i\sin\theta$, we have

$$\cos\theta - i\sin\theta = e^{-i\theta}. \tag{2.7}$$

Adding equations (2.6) and (2.7) gives

$$2\cos\theta = e^{i\theta} + e^{-i\theta}, \tag{2.8}$$

and subtracting them gives

$$2i\sin\theta = e^{i\theta} - e^{-i\theta}. \tag{2.9}$$

Equations (2.8) and (2.9) enable us to express $\cos\theta$ and $\sin\theta$ as combinations of complex exponentials, and it is these equations we use to obtain the identities we are looking for.

Example 2.9

(a) Show that $\cos^4\theta = \dfrac{1}{2^4}(e^{i\theta} + e^{-i\theta})^4$.

(b) Expand the expression $(e^{i\theta} + e^{-i\theta})^4$ using the Binomial Theorem, and hence show that

$$\cos^4\theta = \tfrac{1}{8}(\cos 4\theta + 4\cos 2\theta + 3).$$

Solution

(a) $2\cos\theta = e^{i\theta} + e^{-i\theta}$, so $(2\cos\theta)^4 = (e^{i\theta} + e^{i\theta})^4$.

Hence $\cos^4\theta = \dfrac{1}{2^4}(e^{i\theta} + e^{-i\theta})^4$.

(b) $(e^{i\theta} + e^{-i\theta})^4 = (e^{i\theta})^4 + 4(e^{i\theta})^3(e^{-i\theta})$
$$+ 6(e^{i\theta})^2(e^{-i\theta})^2 + 4(e^{i\theta})(e^{-i\theta})^3 + (e^{-i\theta})^4$$
$$= e^{i4\theta} + 4e^{i2\theta} + 6 + 4e^{-i2\theta} + e^{-i4\theta}.$$

Hence

$$\cos^4\theta = \frac{1}{2^4}(e^{i4\theta} + 4e^{i2\theta} + 6 + 4e^{-i2\theta} + e^{-i4\theta})$$

$$= \frac{1}{2^4}\left((e^{i4\theta} + e^{-i4\theta}) + 4(e^{i2\theta} + e^{-i2\theta}) + 6\right).$$

Using equation (2.8) first with 4θ in place of θ and then with 2θ in place of θ, we have

$$\cos^4\theta = \frac{1}{2^4}(2\cos 4\theta + 8\cos 2\theta + 6) = \frac{1}{8}(\cos 4\theta + 4\cos 2\theta + 3),$$

as required. ■

Exercise 2.22

(a) Show that $\sin^5\theta = \dfrac{1}{2^5 i}(e^{i\theta} - e^{-i\theta})^5$.

(b) Expand $(e^{i\theta} - e^{-i\theta})^5$ using the Binomial Theorem, and hence show that $\sin^5\theta = \frac{1}{16}(\sin 5\theta - 5\sin 3\theta + 10\sin\theta)$.

Further exercises

Exercise 2.23   Let $z_1 = 2 + 3i$ and $z_2 = 1 - 4i$. Find $z_1 + z_2$, $z_1 - z_2$, $z_1 z_2$, $\overline{z_1}$, $\overline{z_2}$, z_1/z_2 and $1/z_1$.

Exercise 2.24   Draw a diagram showing each of the following complex numbers in the complex plane, and express them in polar form, using principal arguments.

(a) $\sqrt{3} - i$ (b) $-5i$ (c) $-2 - 2\sqrt{3}i$

Exercise 2.25   Express each of the following complex numbers in Cartesian form.

(a) $2\sqrt{2}\left(\cos\frac{1}{4}\pi + i\sin\frac{1}{4}\pi\right)$

(b) $3\left(\cos\frac{1}{2}\pi + i\sin\frac{1}{2}\pi\right)$

(c) $\cos\frac{5}{6}\pi + i\sin\frac{5}{6}\pi$

Exercise 2.26   Let $z_1 = \sqrt{3} - i$, $z_2 = -5i$ and $z_3 = -2 - 2\sqrt{3}i$. Use the solution to Exercise 2.24 to determine the following complex numbers in polar form in terms of the principal argument.

(a) $z_1 z_2 z_3$ (b) $\dfrac{z_1 z_2}{z_3}$

Exercise 2.27   Solve the equation $z^5 = -32$, leaving your answers in polar form.

Exercise 2.28   Solve the equation $z^3 + z^2 - z + 15 = 0$, given that one solution is an integer.

Exercise 2.29   Determine a polynomial of degree 4 whose roots are 3, -2, $2 - i$ and $2 + i$.

Exercise 2.30   Use de Moivre's Theorem to obtain formulas for $\cos 6\theta$ and $\sin 6\theta$ in terms of $\cos\theta$ and $\sin\theta$.

Exercise 2.31   Use the definition of e^z to express the following complex numbers in Cartesian form.

(a) $e^{i\pi/2}$ (b) $e^{3+i\pi/4}$ (c) $e^{-1+i\pi}$

3   Modular arithmetic

After working through this section, you should be able to:

(a) explain the terms *modular addition* and *modular multiplication*;

(b) use Euclid's Algorithm to find multiplicative inverses in modular arithmetic, where these exist.

In this section, instead of enlarging the number system $\mathbb{R}$, we do arithmetic with finite sets of integers, namely the sets of possible remainders when we divide by particular positive integers. This type of arithmetic is important in number theory (the study of the integers) and in cryptography. It is used frequently in the group theory units.

3.1 Division

If we divide one positive integer by another we obtain a **quotient** and a **remainder**. For example, 29 divided by 4 gives quotient 7 and remainder 1 because $29 = 7 \times 4 + 1$. If we divide any positive integer by 4, the remainder will be one of the numbers 0, 1, 2, 3.

This idea can be extended to the division of a negative integer by a positive integer. For example, -19 divided by 4 gives quotient -5 and remainder 1 because $-19 = (-5) \times 4 + 1$. If we divide any negative integer by 4, the remainder is again one of the numbers 0, 1, 2, 3.

This result can be generalised to the following theorem.

Theorem 3.1 Division Algorithm

Let a and n be integers, with $n > 0$. Then there are unique integers q and r such that

$$a = qn + r, \quad \text{with } 0 \le r < n.$$

Strictly speaking, this theorem is not an algorithm, but 'division algorithm' is the traditional name for it.

We say that dividing a by the **divisor** n gives **quotient** q and **remainder** r.

We do not give a formal proof of Theorem 3.1, but it can be illustrated as follows. We mark integer multiples of n along the number line as shown in the diagram below, and then observe in which of the resulting intervals of length n the integer a lies. Suppose that a lies in the interval $[qn, (q+1)n)$ so that $qn \le a < (q+1)n$.

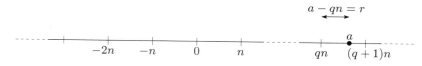

Then, if we let $r = a - qn$, we have $a = qn + r$ and $0 \le r < n$, which is the required result.

Exercise 3.1 For each of the following integers a and n, find the quotient and remainder on division of a by n.

(a) $a = 65, \quad n = 7$ (b) $a = -256, \quad n = 13$

Exercise 3.2

(a) What are the possible remainders on division of an integer by 7?

(b) Find two positive and two negative integers all of which have remainder 3 on division by 7.

3.2 Congruence

The Division Algorithm tells us that, when we divide any integer by a positive integer n, the set of possible remainders is $\{0, 1, 2, \ldots, n-1\}$. Integers which differ by a multiple of n have the same remainder on division by n and are, in this sense, 'the same' as each other. We now introduce some notation and terminology for this idea of 'sameness', which is known as *congruence*.

Definitions Let n be a positive integer. Two integers a and b are **congruent modulo n** if $a - b$ is a multiple of n; that is, if a and b have the same remainder on division by n.

In symbols we write

$$a \equiv b \ (\text{mod } n).$$

Such a statement is called a **congruence**, and n is called the **modulus** of the congruence.

We say 'a is congruent to b modulo n'.

This is a different meaning for the word 'modulus' from others you have met in this course. It is important to interpret technical terms according to their context.

Example 3.1   Which of the following congruences are true, and which are false?

(a) $27 \equiv 5 \ (\text{mod } 11)$ (b) $14 \equiv -6 \ (\text{mod } 3)$

(c) $343 \equiv 207 \ (\text{mod } 68)$ (d) $1 \equiv -1 \ (\text{mod } 2)$

Solution

(a) $27 - 5 = 22$, which is a multiple of 11, so this congruence is true.

Alternatively, we could note that $27 = 2 \times 11 + 5$ and $5 = 0 \times 11 + 5$, so 27 and 5 both have remainder 5 on division by 11.

(b) $14 - (-6) = 20$, which is not a multiple of 3, so this congruence is false.

Alternatively, $14 = 4 \times 3 + 2$ and $-6 = (-2) \times 3 + 0$, so 14 has remainder 2 on division by 3, but -6 has remainder 0.

(c) $343 - 207 = 136 = 2 \times 68$, so this congruence is true.

Alternatively, $343 = 5 \times 68 + 3$ and $207 = 3 \times 68 + 3$, so 343 and 207 both have remainder 3 on division by 68.

(d) $1 - (-1) = 2$, so this congruence is true.

Both 1 and -1 have remainder 1 on division by 2.   ∎

It is often simplest to check a congruence $a \equiv b \ (\text{mod } n)$ by considering the difference $a - b$.

Exercise 3.3   Find the remainder on division by 17 of each of the numbers 25, 53, -15, 3 and 127, and state any congruences modulo 17 that exist between these numbers.

We shall need to use some properties of congruences in the following sections, and we state these properties here.

> **Theorem 3.2 Properties of congruences**
>
> Let n and k be positive integers, and let a, b, c, d be integers. Then
>
> (a) $a \equiv a \pmod{n}$;
>
> (b) if $a \equiv b \pmod{n}$, then $b \equiv a \pmod{n}$;
>
> (c) if $a \equiv b \pmod{n}$ and $b \equiv c \pmod{n}$, then $a \equiv c \pmod{n}$;
>
> (d) if $a \equiv b \pmod{n}$ and $c \equiv d \pmod{n}$, then $a + c \equiv b + d \pmod{n}$;
>
> (e) if $a \equiv b \pmod{n}$ and $c \equiv d \pmod{n}$, then $ac \equiv bd \pmod{n}$;
>
> (f) if $a \equiv b \pmod{n}$, then $a^k \equiv b^k \pmod{n}$.

Although this may seem a long list, these properties are quite simple.

Proof   We prove properties (a)–(d) here and ask you to prove properties (e) and (f) in Exercise 3.4.

(a) $a - a = 0 = 0 \times n$, so $a \equiv a \pmod{n}$.

(b) Suppose that $a \equiv b \pmod{n}$. Then $a - b = kn$ for some integer k. Hence $b - a = (-k)n$, so $b \equiv a \pmod{n}$.

(c) Suppose that $a \equiv b \pmod{n}$ and $b \equiv c \pmod{n}$. Then $a - b = kn$ and $b - c = ln$ for some integers k and l. Hence

$$a - c = a - b + b - c = kn + ln = (k + l)n,$$

so $a \equiv c \pmod{n}$.

(d) If $a \equiv b \pmod{n}$ and $c \equiv d \pmod{n}$, then $a - b = kn$ and $c - d = ln$ for some integers k and l. Hence $a = b + kn$ and $c = d + ln$, so

$$a + c = b + kn + d + ln = b + d + (k + l)n.$$

Hence $(a + c) - (b + d) = (k + l)n$, so $a + c \equiv b + d \pmod{n}$. ∎

Exercise 3.4

(a) Use a similar method to that used in part (d) of the above proof to prove property (e) of Theorem 3.2.

(b) Use property (e) and mathematical induction to prove property (f) of Theorem 3.2.

The properties in Theorem 3.2 are particularly useful when finding the remainder of a large integer on division by another integer.

Example 3.2

(a) Find the remainders of both 2375 and 5421 on division by 22.

(b) Find the remainder of 2375×5421 on division by 22.

(c) Find the remainder of $(2375)^{15}$ on division by 22.

Solution

$(2375)^{15}$ is too large to fit into the memory of most computers, so there is a real advantage in this method.

(a) Using property (c), we can add or subtract any convenient multiples of 22, and make a list of congruences. We have

$$2375 \equiv 175 \equiv 65 \equiv -1 \equiv 21 \pmod{22}$$

and

Here we have subtracted 2200, then 110, then 66; then added 22.

$$5421 \equiv 1021 \equiv 141 \equiv 31 \equiv 9 \pmod{22},$$

so 2375 has remainder 21 on division by 22, and 5421 has remainder 9 on division by 22.

Here we have subtracted 4400, then 880, then 110, then 22.

(b) Using property (e), we obtain

$$2375 \times 5421 \equiv 21 \times 9 \equiv -1 \times 9 \equiv -9 \equiv 13 \pmod{22},$$

so 2375×5421 has remainder 13 on division by 22.

(c) Using property (f), we obtain

$$(2375)^{15} \equiv (-1)^{15} \equiv -1 \equiv 21 \pmod{22},$$

so $(2375)^{15}$ has remainder 21 on division by 22. ∎

3.3 Operations in $\mathbb{Z}_n$ — *integers, modulo n.*

The Division Algorithm tells us that all the possible remainders on division by an integer n lie in the set

$$\{0, 1, \ldots, n-1\}.$$

We denote this set by $\mathbb{Z}_n$. For each integer $n \geq 2$ we have a set $\mathbb{Z}_n$, and it is on these sets that we perform *modular arithmetic*. The modular addition operations $+_n$ and modular multiplication operations $\times_n$ are defined as follows.

Definitions For any integer $n \geq 2$,

$$\mathbb{Z}_n = \{0, 1, \ldots, n-1\}.$$

For a and b in $\mathbb{Z}_n$, the operations $+_{\boldsymbol{n}}$ and $\times_{\boldsymbol{n}}$ are defined by:

$a +_n b$ is the remainder of $a + b$ on division by n;

$a \times_n b$ is the remainder of $a \times b$ on division by n.

The integer n is called the **modulus** for this arithmetic.

$a +_n b$ is read as a plus b $\pmod n$, and may also be written $a + b \pmod n$. Similarly, $a \times_n b$ is read as a times b $\pmod n$ and may also be written as $a \times b \pmod n$.

For example, $\mathbb{Z}_7 = \{0, 1, 2, 3, 4, 5, 6\}$ and we have

$$3 + 6 = 9, \quad \text{so } 3 +_7 6 = 2,$$
$$3 \times 6 = 18, \quad \text{so } 3 \times_7 6 = 4.$$

You have certainly met some modular arithmetic before, as the operations $+_{12}$ and $+_{24}$ are used in measuring time on 12-hour and 24-hour clocks, respectively.

Exercise 3.5 Evaluate the following.

(a) $3 +_5 7, \quad 4 +_{17} 5, \quad 8 +_{16} 12.$

(b) $3 \times_5 7, \quad 4 \times_{17} 5, \quad 8 \times_{16} 12.$

In Sections 1 and 2 we listed some properties satisfied by the real and complex numbers. We now investigate whether the sets $\mathbb{Z}_n$ satisfy similar properties.

We also investigate what equations we can solve in $\mathbb{Z}_n$; for example, can we solve the equations

$$x +_9 3 = 2, \quad x \times_9 3 = 2, \quad x \times_9 x = 2?$$

These may look much simpler than the equations that we were trying to solve in $\mathbb{C}$, but they pose interesting questions. We shall see that the answers may depend on the modulus that we are using.

Before we discuss these questions further, we look at addition and multiplication tables, which provide a convenient way of studying addition and multiplication in $\mathbb{Z}_n$.

We consider addition first. Here are the addition tables for $\mathbb{Z}_4$ and $\mathbb{Z}_7$.

$+_4$	0	1	2	3
0	0	1	2	3
1	1	2	3	0
2	2	3	0	1
3	3	0	1	2

$+_7$	0	1	2	3	4	5	6
0	0	1	2	3	4	5	6
1	1	2	3	4	5	6	0
2	2	3	4	5	6	0	1
3	3	4	5	6	0	1	2
4	4	5	6	0	1	2	3
5	5	6	0	1	2	3	4
6	6	0	1	2	3	4	5

In order to evaluate $4 +_7 2$, say, we look in the row labelled 4 and the column labelled 2 in the second table to obtain the answer 6.

Exercise 3.6

(a) Use the tables above to solve the following equations.

   (i) $x +_4 3 = 2$ (ii) $x +_7 5 = 2$

   (iii) $x +_4 2 = 0$ (iv) $x +_7 5 = 0$

(b) What patterns do you notice in the tables?

Exercise 3.7

(a) Construct the addition table for $\mathbb{Z}_6$.

(b) Solve the equations $x +_6 1 = 5$ and $x +_6 5 = 1$.

For every integer $n \geq 2$, the additive properties of $\mathbb{Z}_n$ are the same as the additive properties of $\mathbb{R}$, as follows.

Addition in $\mathbb{Z}_n$

A1.   If $a, b \in \mathbb{Z}_n$, then
$\qquad a +_n b \in \mathbb{Z}_n$.   CLOSURE

A2.   If $a \in \mathbb{Z}_n$, then
$\qquad a +_n 0 = 0 +_n a = a$.   IDENTITY

A3.   If $a \in \mathbb{Z}_n$, then there is a number $b \in \mathbb{Z}_n$ such that   INVERSES
$\qquad a +_n b = b +_n a = 0$.

A4.   If $a, b, c \in \mathbb{Z}_n$, then
$\qquad (a +_n b) +_n c = a +_n (b +_n c)$.   ASSOCIATIVITY

A5.   If $a, b \in \mathbb{Z}_n$, then
$\qquad a +_n b = b +_n a$.   COMMUTATIVITY

Property A1 follows from the Division Algorithm and the definition of $\mathbb{Z}_n$. The other properties can be deduced from the corresponding properties for integers.

Exercise 3.8   By using the corresponding property for integers, prove property A5.

If $a, b \in \mathbb{Z}_n$ and $a +_n b = 0$, then we say that b is the **additive inverse** of a in $\mathbb{Z}_n$. For example, 4 and 5 belong to $\mathbb{Z}_9$ and $4 +_9 5 = 0$, so 5 is the additive inverse of 4 in $\mathbb{Z}_9$. Property A3 states that every element of $\mathbb{Z}_n$ has an additive inverse in $\mathbb{Z}_n$.

Additive inverses are sometimes written in the form $-_n a$; that is, if $a +_n b = 0$, then we write $b = -_n a$. For example, $5 = -_9 4$.

Exercise 3.9

(a) Use the addition table for $\mathbb{Z}_7$ on page 34 to complete the following table of additive inverses in $\mathbb{Z}_7$.

a	0	1	2	3	4	5	6
$-_7 a$							

(b) Complete the following table of additive inverses in $\mathbb{Z}_n$, explaining why your answers are correct.

a	0	1	2	...	r	...	$n-1$
$-_n a$							

The existence of additive inverses means that, as well as doing addition modulo n, we can also do subtraction. We define $a -_n b$ or, equivalently, $a - b \pmod{n}$, to be the remainder of $a - b$ on division by n.

With this definition, $a -_n b$ is equal to $a +_n (-_n b)$.

For example, to find $2 -_8 7$, we have

$$2 - 7 = -5 \equiv 3 \pmod 8.$$

Since $3 \in \mathbb{Z}_8$, it follows that

$$2 -_8 7 = 3.$$

3.4 Modular multiplication

In the last subsection we stated that, for any integer $n \geq 2$, the set $\mathbb{Z}_n$ satisfies the same rules for addition modulo n as the real numbers satisfy for ordinary addition. When it comes to multiplication in $\mathbb{Z}_n$, *most* of the familiar rules for multiplication of the real numbers are true. In particular, the following properties hold.

Multiplication in $\mathbb{Z}_n$

M1. If $a, b \in \mathbb{Z}_n$, then
$a \times_n b \in \mathbb{Z}_n$.   CLOSURE

M2. If $a \in \mathbb{Z}_n$, then
$a \times_n 1 = 1 \times_n a = a$.   IDENTITY

M4. If $a, b, c \in \mathbb{Z}_n$, then
$(a \times_n b) \times_n c = a \times_n (b \times_n c)$.   ASSOCIATIVITY

M5. If $a, b \in \mathbb{Z}_n$, then
$a \times_n b = b \times_n a$.   COMMUTATIVITY

The following property also holds.

D. If $a, b, c \in \mathbb{Z}_n$, then $a \times_n (b +_n c) = a \times_n b +_n a \times_n c$.   DISTRIBUTIVITY

These properties can be proved in a similar way to the additive properties. You will notice that one property is missing from the list of multiplicative properties; namely, the multiplicative inverse property M3.

We say that b is the **multiplicative inverse** of a in $\mathbb{Z}_n$ if $a, b \in \mathbb{Z}_n$ and $a \times_n b = b \times_n a = 1$. These equations can also be written as $ab \equiv ba \equiv 1 \pmod{n}$. We denote the multiplicative inverse b of a by a^{-1}, when it exists, and it may be referred to as the multiplicative inverse of a modulo n. We now investigate the existence of multiplicative inverses.

For example, from the table for $\mathbb{Z}_7$ below, $3 \times_7 5 = 5 \times_7 3 = 1$, so 5 is the multiplicative inverse of 3 in $\mathbb{Z}_7$.

Here are the multiplication tables for $\mathbb{Z}_4$ and $\mathbb{Z}_7$.

$\times_4$	0	1	2	3
0	0	0	0	0
1	0	1	2	3
2	0	2	0	2
3	0	3	2	1

$\times_7$	0	1	2	3	4	5	6
0	0	0	0	0	0	0	0
1	0	1	2	3	4	5	6
2	0	2	4	6	1	3	5
3	0	3	6	2	5	1	4
4	0	4	1	5	2	6	3
5	0	5	3	1	6	4	2
6	0	6	5	4	3	2	1

Exercise 3.10

(a) Use the tables above to answer the following.

   (i) Which integers in $\mathbb{Z}_4$ have multiplicative inverses?

   (ii) Find the multiplicative inverse of every integer in $\mathbb{Z}_7$ except 0.

(b) Construct a multiplication table for $\mathbb{Z}_{10}$, and decide which integers in $\mathbb{Z}_{10}$ have multiplicative inverses.

From the solution to Exercise 3.10, it is clear that, unlike $\mathbb{R}$ and $\mathbb{C}$, some systems $\mathbb{Z}_n$ contain non-zero elements that do not have a multiplicative inverse. The question of whether an element $a \in \mathbb{Z}_n$ has a multiplicative inverse in $\mathbb{Z}_n$ is connected with the *common factors* of a and n.

Definitions

Two positive integers a and b have a **common factor** c, where c is a positive integer, if a and b are both divisible by c.

Two positive integers a and b are said to be **coprime**, or **relatively prime**, if their only common factor is 1.

The *greatest* common factor of a and b is the largest of their common factors.

Later in this subsection we prove that an element a of $\mathbb{Z}_n$ has a multiplicative inverse in $\mathbb{Z}_n$ if and only if a and n are coprime. First we look at a method for finding multiplicative inverses where they exist. Although we can find such inverses by trial and error, or by writing out the multiplication table for $\mathbb{Z}_n$, as n becomes larger the method illustrated in the following example becomes more efficient. It is known as **Euclid's Algorithm**, and was described in Euclid's *Elements*, which dates from around 300 BC.

Euclid did not express the algorithm in this form, however.

Example 3.3   Find the multiplicative inverse of 10 in $\mathbb{Z}_{27}$.

Solution   We apply the Division Algorithm repeatedly, starting by dividing the modulus 27 by the integer 10, whose multiplicative inverse we seek:

$$27 = 2 \times 10 + 7$$
$$10 = 1 \times 7 + 3 \tag{3.1}$$
$$7 = 2 \times 3 + 1$$
$$3 = 3 \times 1 + 0$$

The first part of the method, consisting of repeated application of the Division Algorithm, is the procedure known as Euclid's Algorithm. When it is applied to any two positive integers a and b, the last but one remainder is the greatest common factor of a and b. The second part of the method, which involves starting with the last but one equation from the first part, is often described as working backwards through Euclid's Algorithm.

At each step we divide the *divisor* in the row above by the *remainder* in the row above, repeating the process until we reach a remainder of 0 (which must occur because the remainders decrease by at least 1 at each step).

Now we use equations (3.1) to find the required multiplicative inverse. Starting with the last but one equation, and working upwards, we have

$$1 = 7 - 2 \times 3$$
$$3 = 10 - 1 \times 7 \tag{3.2}$$
$$7 = 27 - 2 \times 10.$$

We rearrange each equation so that only the remainder is on the left-hand side.

We write down the first of equations (3.2), and use the other two equations to eliminate multiples of 3 and 7 by successive substitutions.

$$1 = 7 - 2 \times 3$$
$$= 7 - 2(10 - 1 \times 7)$$
$$= -2 \times 10 + 3 \times 7$$
$$= -2 \times 10 + 3(27 - 2 \times 10)$$
$$= 3 \times 27 - 8 \times 10.$$

After each substitution, 1 is expressed as a multiple of one integer plus a multiple of another integer, where the two integers are a neighbouring pair from the list 27, 10, 7, 3 of left-hand sides of equations (3.1). The last equation expresses 1 in terms of multiples of the two integers that we started with, 10 and 27. Rearranging this equation gives

The multiples may be negative; for example, -8×10 is a multiple of 10.

$$(-8) \times 10 = (-3) \times 27 + 1,$$

so

$$(-8) \times 10 \equiv 1 \ (\text{mod } 27).$$

Now the integer -8 does not belong to $\mathbb{Z}_{27}$, but, since $-8 \equiv 19 \ (\text{mod } 27)$, we have

$$19 \times 10 \equiv 1 \ (\text{mod } 27)$$

and hence

$$19 \times_{27} 10 = 1.$$

Hence 19 is the multiplicative inverse of 10 in $\mathbb{Z}_{27}$ and we can write $10^{-1} = 19 \ (\text{mod } 27).$ ■

As a check:
$$19 \times 10 = 190$$
$$= 7 \times 27 + 1.$$

Exercise 3.11   Use Euclid's Algorithm to find

(a) the multiplicative inverse of 7 in $\mathbb{Z}_{16}$;

(b) the multiplicative inverse of 8 in $\mathbb{Z}_{51}$.

We now use Euclid's Algorithm to prove our main result.

> **Theorem 3.3**   Let n and a be positive integers, with a in $\mathbb{Z}_n$. Then a has a multiplicative inverse in $\mathbb{Z}_n$ if and only if a and n are coprime.

Proof   First we prove the 'if' part; that is, a has a multiplicative inverse in $\mathbb{Z}_n$ if a and n are coprime.

We use Euclid's Algorithm repeatedly and show that, if a and n are coprime, then the final remainder before we reach 0 must be 1.

Let

$$
\begin{aligned}
n &= q_1 a + r_1 & 0 < r_1 < a \\
a &= q_2 r_1 + r_2 & 0 < r_2 < r_1 \\
r_1 &= q_3 r_2 + r_3 & 0 < r_3 < r_2 \\
&\;\;\vdots & \vdots \\
r_{m-2} &= q_m r_{m-1} + r_m & 0 < r_m < r_{m-1} \\
r_{m-1} &= q_{m+1} r_m + 0.
\end{aligned}
$$

Since the remainders decrease by at least 1 with each step, they must eventually reach 0.

The final equation shows that r_m is a factor of r_{m-1}, and thus the penultimate equation shows that r_m is a factor of r_{m-2}, and so on. Continuing in this way, we find that r_m is a factor of all the remainders, and so of both a and n. Since a and n were assumed to be coprime, we deduce that $r_m = 1$.

Therefore we have, from the penultimate equation,

$$1 = r_{m-2} - q_m r_{m-1}$$

and, by successively substituting for the remainders, we find that there are integers k and d such that $1 = kn + da$. Hence $da = -kn + 1$, so $d \times_n a = 1$.

It is possible that d does not belong to $\mathbb{Z}_n$, but in that case $d \equiv b$ for some $b \in \mathbb{Z}_n$, where $b \neq 0$, so we also have $b \times_n a = 1$.

Hence a has a multiplicative inverse b in $\mathbb{Z}_n$; we write $b = a^{-1} \pmod{n}$.

Now we prove the 'only if' part; that is, a has a multiplicative inverse in $\mathbb{Z}_n$ only if a and n are coprime.

Suppose that a has a multiplicative inverse in $\mathbb{Z}_n$; that is, there is a number b such that $b \times_n a = 1$. Then $ba = kn + 1$ for some integer k, so $ba - kn = 1$.

If a and n have a common factor c, say, then c is a factor of $ba - kn$ and hence of 1. Therefore c can only be 1, so a and n are coprime.   ■

Theorem 3.3 gives us an important corollary in the case when the modulus n is a prime number.

> **Corollary**   Let p be a prime number. Then every non-zero element in $\mathbb{Z}_p$ has a multiplicative inverse in $\mathbb{Z}_p$.

Proof   If p is prime, then every non-zero element in $\mathbb{Z}_p$ is coprime with p, and so has a multiplicative inverse in $\mathbb{Z}_p$ by Theorem 3.3.   ∎

It follows that if we take multiplication in $\mathbb{Z}_p$, where p is prime, then we can add the following property to the list of properties for multiplication in $\mathbb{Z}_n$:

See page 35.

INVERSES

M3.   If $a \in \mathbb{Z}_p$, and $a \neq 0$, then a has a multiplicative inverse $a^{-1} \in \mathbb{Z}_p$ such that $a \times_p a^{-1} = a^{-1} \times_p a = 1$.

But this property does not hold for $\mathbb{Z}_n$ if n is not prime, as in that case some elements $a \in \mathbb{Z}_n$ do not have multiplicative inverses.

We now return briefly to the question of whether we can solve equations in modular arithmetic. We begin by considering linear equations, that is, equations of the form

$$a \times_n x = c, \tag{3.3}$$

where $a, c \in \mathbb{Z}_n$. We seek all solutions $x \in \mathbb{Z}_n$.

First we consider the case where a and n are coprime. In this case, by Theorem 3.3, a has a multiplicative inverse a^{-1} and we can solve equation (3.3) by multiplying both sides by this inverse.

Example 3.4   Solve the equation $10 \times_{27} x = 14$.

Solution   In Example 3.3 we found that the multiplicative inverse of 10 in $\mathbb{Z}_{27}$ is 19. Hence we have

$$
\begin{aligned}
10 \times_{27} x = 14 &\Leftrightarrow 10^{-1} \times_{27} (10 \times_{27} x) = 10^{-1} \times_{27} 14 \\
&\Leftrightarrow (10^{-1} \times_{27} 10) \times_{27} x = 19 \times_{27} 14 \\
&\Leftrightarrow x = 23,
\end{aligned}
$$

so the given equation has the unique solution $x = 23$.   ∎

In general, by an argument similar to that of Example 3.4, if a and n are coprime, then equation (3.3) has the *unique* solution $x = a^{-1} \times_n c$.

> **Exercise 3.12**   Use the method of Example 3.4 and the solution to Exercise 3.11 to solve the following equations.
>
> (a) $7 \times_{16} x = 3$ (b) $8 \times_{51} x = 19$

In particular, if a and n are coprime, then equation (3.3) has a solution for *every* $c \in \mathbb{Z}_n$, so *every* element of $\mathbb{Z}_n$ appears in the row labelled a of the multiplication table for $\mathbb{Z}_n$.

To use the method of Example 3.4, first we need to find the multiplicative inverse in $\mathbb{Z}_n$ of the coefficient a of x. If we have not already found this inverse (for example, by using Euclid's Algorithm), and the modulus n is fairly small, then the quickest way to solve the equation may be just to try different values of x. We know that there is a unique solution, so we can stop trying values once we have found a solution. Sometimes a solution can be spotted by using conguences.

Example 3.5   Solve the equation $5 \times_{12} x = 7$.

Solution   Observe that $7 \equiv -5 \pmod{12}$, so we have

$$5 \times (-1) \equiv 7 \pmod{12}.$$

The integer -1 is not an element of $\mathbb{Z}_{12}$, but $-1 \equiv 11 \pmod{12}$, so

$$5 \times 11 \equiv 7 \pmod{12}; \quad \text{that is,} \quad 5 \times_{12} 11 = 7.$$

Hence the solution of the given equation is $x = 11$.   ∎

Now consider equation (3.3) in the case where a and n are not coprime: suppose that a and n have a common factor $d \geq 2$. Then equation (3.3) has a solution only if d is also a factor of c. To see this, notice that equation (3.3) is equivalent to

$$ax = kn + c, \quad \text{for some } k \in \mathbb{Z}.$$

If there exists an integer solution $x = b$ of this equation, then

$$c = ab - kn$$

and, since d is a factor of both a and n, it follows that d is a factor of c.

If a, n and c have a common factor $d \geq 2$, then equation (3.3) has more than one solution. In fact, although we do not prove it here, if d is the *greatest* common factor of a, n and c, then equation (3.3) has d solutions, given by

$$x = b, \quad x = b + n/d, \quad x = b + 2n/d, \quad \ldots, \quad x = b + (d-1)n/d,$$

where $x = b$ is the smallest solution. That is, we add multiples of n/d to the smallest solution.

There is a method for finding the smallest solution which is similar to the method used in Example 3.4 for the case where a and n are coprime, but we do not cover it in this course. If n is fairly small, then we can find the smallest solution by trying values. Alternatively, it may be possible to spot a solution, but as this may not be the smallest solution, we may need to subtract multiples of n/d as well as, or instead of, adding them.

Thus if a and n have a common factor $d \geq 2$, then all the elements in the row labelled a of the multiplication table for $\mathbb{Z}_n$ have common factor d.

You can prove that these are solutions by using substitution. For example, $x = b + n/d$ is a solution because

$$a \times_n (b + n/d)$$
$$= a \times_n (b +_n n/d)$$
$$= a \times_n b +_n a \times_n n/d$$
$$= c +_n (a/d) \times n = c,$$

where the last but one line follows because $x = b$ is a solution and $a/d \in \mathbb{Z}_n$.

Example 3.6   Solve each of the following equations.

(a) $4 \times_{12} x = 6$ (b) $4 \times_{12} x = 8$

Solution

(a) This equation has no solutions, since 4 is a factor of both 4 and 12 but is not a factor of 6.

(b) One solution of this equation is $x = 2$. Also $n/d = 12/4 = 3$, so the other solutions are $x = 2 + 3 = 5$ and $x = 2 + 2 \times 3 = 8$. ■ $\cancel{x = 2 + 3 \times 3 = 11}$

Exercise 3.13   Find all the solutions of the following equations.

(a) In $\mathbb{Z}_{12}$: $3 \times_{12} x = 6$, $8 \times_{12} x = 7$, $5 \times_{12} x = 2$.

(b) In $\mathbb{Z}_{16}$: $4 \times_{16} x = 12$, $3 \times_{16} x = 13$, $8 \times_{16} x = 2$.

Near the beginning of Subsection 3.3 we posed the question: can we solve the equation $x \times_9 x = 2$? That is, is there an element of $\mathbb{Z}_9$ whose square is 2?

See page 33.

Example 3.7   Show that there is no element of $\mathbb{Z}_9$ whose square is 2.

Solution   We solve this problem by exhaustion, by writing down the squares of all the elements of $\mathbb{Z}_9$.

x	0	1	2	3	4	5	6	7	8
$x \times_9 x$	0	1	4	0	7	7	0	4	1

We can see from this table that there is no element of $\mathbb{Z}_9$ whose square is 2. In fact, we can go further and say that the remainder of a square modulo 9 can be only 0, 1, 4 or 7. That is, 0, 1, 4 and 7 are the only elements of $\mathbb{Z}_9$ that are squares of other elements. ■

Exercise 3.14

(a) Find all the solutions of the equation $x \times_8 x = 4$.

(b) Find all the values of c in $\mathbb{Z}_8$ for which it is possible to solve the equation $x \times_8 x = c$.

In general, the solution of quadratic equations in modular arithmetic is more complicated than that of linear equations. You will study this topic further if you take a course in number theory.

Further exercises

Exercise 3.15   Evaluate the following sums and products in modular arithmetic.

(a) $21 +_{26} 15$, $21 \times_{26} 15$.

(b) $19 +_{33} 14$, $19 \times_{33} 14$.

Exercise 3.16   Use Euclid's Algorithm to find:

(a) the multiplicative inverse of 8 in $\mathbb{Z}_{21}$; 8

(b) the multiplicative inverse of 19 in $\mathbb{Z}_{33}$. 7

Exercise 3.17   Construct the multiplication table for $\mathbb{Z}_{11}$, and hence find the multiplicative inverse of every non-zero element in $\mathbb{Z}_{11}$.

Exercise 3.18   Use the solution to Exercise 3.16 to solve the following equations.

(a) $8 \times_{21} x = 13$ (b) $19 \times_{33} x = 15$

Exercise 3.19   Find all the solutions of the following equations.

(a) In $\mathbb{Z}_8$: $3 \times_8 x = 7$, $4 \times_8 x = 7$, $4 \times_8 x = 4$.

(b) In $\mathbb{Z}_{15}$: $3 \times_{15} x = 6$, $4 \times_{15} x = 3$, $5 \times_{15} x = 2$.

Exercise 3.20

(a) Show that the equation $x \times_{12} x = 7$ has no solutions.

(b) Find all the solutions of $x \times_{12} x = 4$.

4   Equivalence relations

After working through this section, you should be able to:

(a) explain the meanings of a *relation* defined on a set, an *equivalence relation* and a *partition* of a set;

(b) determine whether a given relation defined on a given set is an equivalence relation by checking the *reflexive, symmetric* and *transitive properties*;

(c) understand that an equivalence relation partitions a set into *equivalence classes*;

(d) determine the equivalence classes for a given equivalence relation.

4.1 What is a relation?

In this final section we look at a method of classifying the elements of a set by sorting them into subsets. We shall require that the set is sorted into disjoint subsets—so each element of the set belongs to *exactly one* subset. Such a classification is known as a *partition* of a set. In order to achieve a partition, we need to have a method which enables us to decide whether or not one element belongs to the same subset as another. We look first at the general idea of a *relation*, and then at the particular properties needed by a relation in order to partition a set. A relation which satisfies these special properties is known as an *equivalence relation*, and the subsets into which the set is partitioned are called *equivalence classes*.

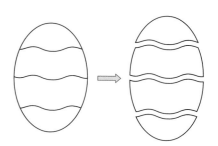

Equivalence relations occur in all branches of mathematics. For example, in geometry, two possible relations between the set of all triangles in the plane are *is congruent to* and *is similar to*. These are both equivalence relations: the relation *is congruent to* partitions the set of triangles into classes such that all the triangles within each class are congruent to each other, whereas *is similar to* partitions the set into classes of similar triangles. These partitions are different: triangles of the same shape but different sizes are similar to, but not congruent to, each other.

Equivalence relations are not confined to sets of mathematical objects. For example, relations between people such as *is the same height as* and *has the same birthday as* are equivalence relations.

Relations

We shall use the symbol $\sim$ (known as tilde or twiddle) to represent a *relation* between two elements of a set.

> **Definition** We say that $\sim$ is a **relation** on a set X if, whenever $x, y \in X$, the statement $x \sim y$ is either true or false.
>
>   If $x \sim y$ is true, then x is related to y.
>
>   If $x \sim y$ is false, then x is not related to y and we write $x \nsim y$.

Some texts use ρ, rather than $\sim$, for an arbitrary relation. Certain relations have special symbols; for example,

  $<$ means *is less than*,
  $=$ means *is equal to*.

The statement $x \sim y$ can be read as 'x is related to y' or 'x twiddles y'.

Examples

1. The condition 'is equal to' is a relation on any set of real numbers because, for any x, y in the set, the statement 'x is equal to y' is either definitely true or definitely false. This relation is usually denoted by the symbol $=$. For this relation, each real number in the set is related only to itself!

2. The condition 'is less than' is a relation on any set of real numbers, and we usually denote it by the symbol $<$. For example, $-2 < 1$, but $1 \nless -2$ and $3 \nless 3$.

3. The condition 'is the derivative of' is a relation on any set of functions. We can define

    $g \sim f$ if g is the derivative of f.

    For example, let $f(x) = x^3$, $g(x) = 3x^2$ and $h(x) = 2e^x$. Then $g \sim f$ because g is the derivative of f, and $h \sim h$ because h is the derivative of h, but $f \nsim g$ because f is not the derivative of g.

4. On $\mathbb{C}$, we can define a relation

$$z_1 \sim z_2 \quad \text{if } |z_1 - z_2| \le 4;$$

that is, z_1 is related to z_2 if the distance between z_1 and z_2 in the complex plane is less than or equal to 4. For example, $1 + i \sim 2 - i$ because

$$|(1 + i) - (2 - i)| = |-1 + 2i| = \sqrt{5} \le 4,$$

but $1 + i \nsim 3 + 5i$ because

$$|(1 + i) - (3 + 5i)| = |-2 - 4i| = \sqrt{20} > 4.$$

4.2 Equivalence relations

Our formal definition of an equivalence relation involves three key properties. A relation that has these three properties partitions the set on which the relation is defined, as we show later in this subsection.

Definition   An **equivalence relation** on a set X is a relation $\sim$ on X which satisfies the following three properties.

E1 REFLEXIVE   For all $x \in X$,

$$x \sim x.$$

E2 SYMMETRIC   For all $x, y \in X$,

$$\text{if } x \sim y, \text{ then } y \sim x.$$

E3 TRANSITIVE   For all $x, y, z \in X$,

$$\text{if } x \sim y \text{ and } y \sim z, \text{ then } x \sim z.$$

The three properties can easily be remembered by the letters R, S and T.

x is related to itself.

If x is related to y, then y is related to x.

If x is related to y and y is related to z, then x is related to z.

The reflexive, symmetric and transitive properties are independent, in the sense that relations exist with every combination of these properties. (However, relations which are symmetric and transitive but not reflexive are usually somewhat contrived.)

If a relation $\sim$ is symmetric, then 'x is related to y' means the same as 'y is related to x', and we can use either phrase, or simply say 'x and y are related'; we can write either $x \sim y$ or $y \sim x$.

We now consider the examples in the previous subsection to see whether they satisfy any or all of the three properties.

Examples

1. The relation 'is equal to' on $\mathbb{R}$ is reflexive, symmetric and transitive.

   It is reflexive since, for all $x \in \mathbb{R}$, $x = x$.

   It is symmetric since, for all $x, y \in \mathbb{R}$, if $x = y$, then $y = x$.

   It is transitive since, for all $x, y, z \in \mathbb{R}$, if $x = y$ and $y = z$, then $x = z$.

   Hence this relation is an equivalence relation.

2. The relation 'is less than' on $\mathbb{R}$ is neither reflexive (since it is not true that $x < x$ for all $x \in \mathbb{R}$) nor symmetric (since, if $x < y$, then it does not follow that $y < x$), but it is transitive, since, if $x < y$ and $y < z$, then $x < z$.

3. The relation 'is the derivative of' on a set of functions has none of the reflexive, symmetric and transitive properties.

4. The relation defined on $\mathbb{C}$ by

$$z_1 \sim z_2 \quad \text{if } |z_1 - z_2| \le 4$$

is reflexive, since $|z - z| = 0 \le 4$ for all $z \in \mathbb{C}$. It is also symmetric, since, if $|z_1 - z_2| \le 4$, then $|z_2 - z_1| = |z_1 - z_2| \le 4$. However, it is not transitive. The counter-example $z_1 = 0$, $z_2 = 4$, $z_3 = 4 + i$ shows that property E3 fails:

$$|z_1 - z_2| = |0 - 4| = 4 \le 4, \quad \text{so } z_1 \sim z_2,$$
$$|z_2 - z_3| = |4 - (4 + i)| = |i| = 1 \le 4, \quad \text{so } z_2 \sim z_3,$$
$$\text{but } |z_1 - z_3| = |0 - (4 + i)| = |-4 - i| = \sqrt{17} > 4, \quad \text{so } z_1 \nsim z_3.$$

So only the first of the four examples above is an equivalence relation.

Example 4.1   Prove that the relation defined on $\mathbb{C}$ by

$$z_1 \sim z_2 \quad \text{if } |z_1| = |z_2|$$

is an equivalence relation on $\mathbb{C}$.

Solution   We show that properties E1, E2 and E3 hold.

E1 REFLEXIVE   Let $z \in \mathbb{C}$. Then $|z| = |z|$, so $z \sim z$. Thus the relation is reflexive.

E2 SYMMETRIC   Let $z_1, z_2 \in \mathbb{C}$, and suppose that $z_1 \sim z_2$. Then $|z_1| = |z_2|$. Hence $|z_2| = |z_1|$, so $z_2 \sim z_1$. Thus the relation is symmetric.

E3 TRANSITIVE   Let $z_1, z_2, z_3 \in \mathbb{C}$, and suppose that $z_1 \sim z_2$ and $z_2 \sim z_3$. Then $|z_1| = |z_2|$ and $|z_2| = |z_3|$. It follows that $|z_1| = |z_3|$, so $z_1 \sim z_3$. Thus the relation is transitive.

Hence this relation is an equivalence relation.   ∎

Exercise 4.1   For each set A and given relation, decide whether the relation $\sim$ has the reflexive, symmetric and transitive properties, and thus whether it is an equivalence relation. For each property, either prove that it holds or give a counter-example to show that it does not hold.

(a) $A = \mathbb{Z}$; $x \sim y$ if $x - y$ is odd.

(b) $A = \mathbb{Z}$; $x \sim y$ if $x - y$ is even.

(c) A is the set of all lines in the plane; $\ell_1 \sim \ell_2$ if the lines ℓ_1 and ℓ_2 are parallel. (Take the definition of parallel to be 'in the same direction as'.)

(d) $A = \mathbb{C}$; $z_1 \sim z_2$ if $z_1 - z_2$ is real.

At the beginning of this section we stated that we were looking at a method of classifying objects in a set by *partitioning* them.

Definition   A collection of non-empty subsets of a set is a **partition** of the set if every two subsets in the collection are disjoint and the union of all the subsets in the collection is the whole set.

Two sets are *disjoint* if they have no elements in common.

We now show why an equivalence relation partitions the set on which the relation is defined. First we need another definition.

> **Definition**   Let $\sim$ be an equivalence relation defined on a set X; then the **equivalence class** of $x \in X$, denoted by $[\![x]\!]$, is the set
>
> $$[\![x]\!] = \{y \in X : x \sim y\}.$$

Thus $[\![x]\!]$ is the set of all elements in X related to x.

Example 4.2   Find the equivalence classes for the following equivalence relations:

(a) 'is equal to' on a set of real numbers;

(b) the relation of Example 4.1: $z_1 \sim z_2$ if $|z_1| = |z_2|$, on the set $\mathbb{C}$.

Solution

(a) Since $x = y$ only if y is the same real number as x, the equivalence class of the real number x contains only the number x itself. So here each element lies in a single-element equivalence class.

(b) The equivalence class of a particular complex number z_0, say, is $[\![z_0]\!] = \{z \in \mathbb{C} : z \sim z_0\}$. Now $z \sim z_0$ means that $|z| = |z_0|$, so $[\![z_0]\!] = \{z \in \mathbb{C} : |z| = |z_0|\}$. Hence the equivalence class of z_0 is the set of all complex numbers with the same modulus as z_0. If $|z_0| = r$, say, then $[\![z_0]\!] = \{z \in \mathbb{C} : |z| = r\}$; this set forms the circle with centre 0 and radius r in the complex plane. Hence the equivalence classes for this relation are circles with centre 0. (The origin is an equivalence class containing just the complex number $0 + 0i$; it can be thought of as a circle of radius 0.) ∎

> **Theorem 4.1**   The equivalence classes associated with an equivalence relation on a set X have the following properties.
>
> (a) Each $x \in X$ is in an equivalence class.
>
> (b) For all $x, y \in X$, the equivalence classes $[\![x]\!]$ and $[\![y]\!]$ are either equal or disjoint.
>
> Thus the equivalence classes form a partition of X.

Equivalence classes (being sets) are equal if they have exactly the same elements.

Proof   Let $\sim$ be an equivalence relation on a set X.

(a) Let $x \in X$. The relation $\sim$ is reflexive, so $x \sim x$, and hence x belongs to the equivalence class $[\![x]\!]$.

(b) Let $[\![x]\!]$ and $[\![y]\!]$ be equivalence classes with at least one element a in common. Then, since $[\![x]\!]$ and $[\![y]\!]$ are not disjoint, we have to prove that they are equal.

First we show that $[\![x]\!] \subseteq [\![y]\!]$. Suppose that $b \in [\![x]\!]$; we have to show that $b \in [\![y]\!]$. Since $a \in [\![y]\!]$, $a \in [\![x]\!]$ and $b \in [\![x]\!]$, we have

$$y \sim a, \quad a \sim x \quad \text{and} \quad x \sim b, \tag{4.1}$$

respectively. (By definition, $a \in [\![x]\!]$ implies that $x \sim a$, but since $\sim$ is symmetric, this means the same as $a \sim x$.)

Since $\sim$ is transitive, the first two statements of statements (4.1) together imply that $y \sim x$, and this, together with the third statement of statements (4.1), implies that $y \sim b$. Hence $b \in [\![y]\!]$.

This shows that $[\![x]\!] \subseteq [\![y]\!]$. We can show similarly that $[\![y]\!] \subseteq [\![x]\!]$ (we interchange the roles of x and y in the proof that $[\![x]\!] \subseteq [\![y]\!]$). Hence $[\![x]\!] = [\![y]\!]$. ∎

As an illustration of Theorem 4.1, consider the equivalence relation in Example 4.2(b). We saw that the equivalence classes of this relation are of the form

$$\{z \in \mathbb{C} : |z| = r\},$$

where $r \in \mathbb{R}$. That is, this relation partitions the complex plane into concentric circles with centre the origin.

Here we think of the class containing the origin alone as a circle of radius 0.

It follows from Theorem 4.1 that if two elements x and y are related by an equivalence relation, then $[\![x]\!] = [\![y]\!]$. Thus, in general, there is more than one way to denote each equivalence class using the notation $[\![\ ]\!]$: a class can be denoted by $[\![x]\!]$ where x is any one of its elements. It is sometimes useful to choose a particular element x in each equivalence class and denote the class by $[\![x]\!]$. The element x that we choose is called a *representative* of the class.

For example,

$$\{z \in \mathbb{C} : |z| = 4\}$$

is one of the equivalence classes of the equivalence relation in Example 4.2(b). This class contains 4, $-4i$ and $2\sqrt{2} + 2\sqrt{2}i$, for example, so we could denote it by any of $[\![4]\!]$, $[\![-4i]\!]$ or $[\![2\sqrt{2} + 2\sqrt{2}i]\!]$. We might decide to choose the representative 4 and denote the class by $[\![4]\!]$. In general, the equivalence class

$$\{z \in \mathbb{C} : |z| = r\},$$

from Example 4.2(b) contains the element r and so can be denoted by $[\![r]\!]$.

Exercise 4.2   Determine the equivalence classes for the equivalence relations in Exercise 4.1(b), (c) and (d).

The solutions to Exercises 4.1(b) and 4.2 show that the relation on $\mathbb{Z}$ given by

$$x \sim y \quad \text{if } x - y \text{ is even}$$

is an equivalence relation, with equivalence classes

$$[\![0]\!] = \{\ldots, -4, -2, 0, 2, 4, \ldots\}$$

and

$$[\![1]\!] = \{\ldots, -3, -1, 1, 3, \ldots\};$$

that is, the even integers form one class and the odd integers the other. You have already met this idea in Section 3: the relation '$x \sim y$ if $x - y$ is even' is congruence modulo 2.

For any n, congruence modulo n on $\mathbb{Z}$, given by

$$a \sim b \quad \text{if } a \equiv b \ (\text{mod } n),$$

is an equivalence relation; the first three properties given in Theorem 3.2 are the reflexive, symmetric and transitive properties. The equivalence classes for this relation are the sets

$$[\![0]\!] = \{\ldots, -2n, -n, 0, n, 2n, \ldots\},$$
$$[\![1]\!] = \{\ldots, 1 - 2n, 1 - n, 1, 1 + n, 1 + 2n, \ldots\},$$
$$\vdots$$
$$[\![n - 1]\!] = \{\ldots, -n - 1, -1, n - 1, 2n - 1, 3n - 1 \ldots\}.$$

The representatives that we have used to denote the classes are $0, 1, 2, \ldots, n - 1$, which are the elements of $\mathbb{Z}_n$. Thus $\mathbb{Z}_n$ is a *set of representatives* of the equivalence classes of congruence modulo n; that is, each equivalence class has exactly one representative in the set $\mathbb{Z}_n$. The definitions of the modular operations $+_n$ and $\times_n$ can be rephrased using the idea of equivalence classes as follows: for all $a, b \in \mathbb{Z}_n$,

$a +_n b$ is the integer in $\mathbb{Z}_n$ that lies in the class $[\![a + b]\!]$,

$a \times_n b$ is the integer in $\mathbb{Z}_n$ that lies in the class $[\![a \times b]\!]$.

For example, in $\mathbb{Z}_5$,

$3 +_5 4 = 2$

because $3 + 4 = 7$ and the equivalence class $[\![7]\!]$ of congruence modulo 5 contains the element 2 of $\mathbb{Z}_5$.

So far, we have taken congruences only on $\mathbb{Z}$, but it is possible to take congruences also on $\mathbb{R}$, and the modulus does not need to be an integer.

Example 4.3   Show that the relation defined on $\mathbb{R}$ by

$x \sim y$ if $x - y = 2\pi n$, where n is an integer,

is an equivalence relation, and describe the equivalence classes.

Solution   We show that properties E1, E2 and E3 hold.

E1 REFLEXIVE   For each $x \in \mathbb{R}$, we have $x - x = 0 = 2\pi \times 0$, so $x \sim x$ and the relation is reflexive.

E2 SYMMETRIC   Let $x, y \in \mathbb{R}$, and suppose that $x \sim y$. Then $x - y = 2\pi n$, where n is an integer. It follows that $y - x = 2\pi(-n)$, so $y \sim x$. Thus the relation is symmetric.

E3 TRANSITIVE   Let $x, y, z \in \mathbb{R}$, and suppose that $x \sim y$ and $y \sim z$. Then $x - y = 2\pi n$ and $y - z = 2\pi m$, where m and n are integers. It follows that

$$x - z = x - y + y - z = 2\pi(n + m),$$

so $x \sim z$ and thus the relation is transitive.

The equivalence class $[\![r]\!]$ of any real number r is the set of all real numbers related to r by $\sim$; that is, $[\![r]\!]$ is the set of all real numbers that differ from r by a multiple of 2π. So

$[\![r]\!] = \{\ldots, r - 4\pi, r - 2\pi, r, r + 2\pi, r + 4\pi, \ldots\}$.   ■

The equivalence relation in Example 4.3 is congruence modulo 2π. For example,

$\frac{9}{2}\pi \sim \frac{1}{2}\pi$,

and we write

$\frac{9}{2}\pi \equiv \frac{1}{2}\pi \pmod{2\pi}$

because

$\frac{9}{2}\pi - \frac{1}{2}\pi = 2 \times 2\pi$.

We have seen that congruence modulo n on $\mathbb{Z}$ corresponds to modular arithmetic on $\mathbb{Z}_n$, which is a set of representatives of the equivalence classes of congruence modulo n. In a similar way, congruence modulo 2π on $\mathbb{R}$ corresponds to modular arithmetic on a set of representatives of the equivalence classes of congruence modulo 2π. A suitable set of representatives is the interval $(-\pi, \pi]$, since every equivalence class has exactly one representative in this interval. We define modular operations $+_{2\pi}$ and $\times_{2\pi}$ on the interval $(-\pi, \pi]$ as follows: for all $x, y \in (-\pi, \pi]$,

> $x +_{2\pi} y$ is the real number in $(-\pi, \pi]$ that lies in the class $[\![x + y]\!]$,
>
> $x \times_{2\pi} y$ is the real number in $(-\pi, \pi]$ that lies in the class $[\![xy]\!]$.

Other intervals can be used, for example $[0, 2\pi)$, but $(-\pi, \pi]$ is useful as it corresponds to our definition of the principal argument of a complex number.

For example,

$$\pi +_{2\pi} \tfrac{1}{2}\pi = -\tfrac{1}{2}\pi.$$

$\pi + \tfrac{1}{2}\pi = \tfrac{3}{2}\pi$ and $[\![\tfrac{3}{2}\pi]\!]$ contains $-\tfrac{1}{2}\pi$.

This is effectively what we do when we take the *principal* argument of a complex number arising from some calculation.

Arithmetic modulo 2π on the interval $(-\pi, \pi]$ gives us a concise way to express some results about complex numbers. For example, we saw earlier that, if z_1 and z_2 are any two complex numbers, then $\operatorname{Arg} z_1 + \operatorname{Arg} z_2$ is an argument of $z_1 z_2$, but is not necessarily the principal argument. The principal argument is $\operatorname{Arg} z_1 +_{2\pi} \operatorname{Arg} z_2$, so we can now state that

Recall that $\operatorname{Arg} z$ denotes the principal argument of z.

$$\operatorname{Arg}(z_1 z_2) = \operatorname{Arg} z_1 +_{2\pi} \operatorname{Arg} z_2.$$

Further exercises

Exercise 4.3 Let $\sim$ be the relation defined on $\mathbb{Z}$ by

> $x \sim y$ if $2x - y$ is divisible by 7.

Give counter-examples to show that $\sim$ is not reflexive, symmetric or transitive.

Exercise 4.4 Let A be the set of all functions with domain and codomain $\mathbb{R}$, and let $\sim$ be the relation defined on A by

> $f \sim g$ if $f(0) = g(0)$.

Show that this is an equivalence relation and describe the equivalence classes.

Exercise 4.5 Let $\sim$ be the relation defined on $\mathbb{C}$ by

> $z_1 \sim z_2$ if $x_1 - x_2 = 5(y_1 - y_2)$,

where

> $z_1 = x_1 + iy_1, \quad z_2 = x_2 + iy_2.$

Show that this is an equivalence relation and describe the equivalence classes.

Solutions to the exercises

1.1 Suppose that there exists a rational number x such that $x^3 = 2$. We can write $x = p/q$, where p and q are positive integers whose greatest common factor is 1. Then the equation $x^3 = 2$ becomes

$$p^3 = 2q^3.$$

Now the cube of an odd number is odd because

$$(2k+1)^3 = 8k^3 + 12k^2 + 6k + 1$$
$$= 2(4k^3 + 6k^2 + 3k) + 1,$$

so p must be even. If we write $p = 2r$, then our equation becomes

$$(2r)^3 = 2q^3,$$

so we have

$$q^3 = 4r^3.$$

Hence q is also even, so 2 is a common factor of p and q. This contradiction shows that such a number x cannot exist.

1.2 (a) There is no integer 2^{-1} such that $2 \times 2^{-1} = 2^{-1} \times 2 = 1$, for example.

(b) The numbers 1 and -1 both have a multiplicative inverse in $\mathbb{Z}$. In each case the number is its own inverse; such a number is sometimes described as being *self-inverse*.

1.3 (a)
$$x^2 - 7x + 12 = 0$$
$$\Leftrightarrow (x-4)(x-3) = 0$$
$$\Leftrightarrow x = 4 \text{ or } x = 3$$

This equation has two solutions in $\mathbb{R}$.

(b) $x^2 + 6x + 9 = 0$
$$\Leftrightarrow (x+3)^2 = 0$$
$$\Leftrightarrow x = -3$$

This equation has one solution in $\mathbb{R}$.

(c) $2x^2 + 5x - 3 = 0$
$$\Leftrightarrow (2x-1)(x+3) = 0$$
$$\Leftrightarrow x = \tfrac{1}{2} \text{ or } x = -3$$

This equation has two solutions in $\mathbb{R}$.

(d) $2x^2 - 2x - 1 = 0$
$$\Leftrightarrow x = \frac{2 \pm \sqrt{4+8}}{4} = \frac{1}{2} \pm \frac{1}{2}\sqrt{3}$$

This equation has two solutions in $\mathbb{R}$.

(e) $x^2 - 2x + 5 = 0$
$$\Leftrightarrow x = \frac{2 \pm \sqrt{4-20}}{2}$$

Since $4 - 20 = -16$, which is negative, this equation has no solutions in $\mathbb{R}$.

1.4 (a) $x = -2$, which belongs to $\mathbb{Z}$ (and hence to $\mathbb{Q}$ and $\mathbb{R}$).

(b) $x = -\dfrac{7}{\sqrt{3}}$, which belongs to $\mathbb{R}$.

(c) $x = 3$, which belongs to $\mathbb{N}$ (and hence to $\mathbb{Z}$, $\mathbb{Q}$ and $\mathbb{R}$).

(d) $x = -\frac{1}{5}$, which belongs to $\mathbb{Q}$ (and hence to $\mathbb{R}$).

Remark Each linear equation with coefficients in $\mathbb{Q}$ has a solution in $\mathbb{Q}$ (because the equation $ax + b = 0$ where $a, b \in \mathbb{Q}$ and $a \neq 0$ has solution $x = -b/a$, which involves only additive inverses and division of rational numbers). Similarly each linear equation with coefficients in $\mathbb{R}$ has a solution in $\mathbb{R}$. The same is not true of $\mathbb{Z}$, as part (d) illustrates.

1.5 Suppose there is a rational number x such that $x^2 = 3$. Then we can write $x = p/q$, where p and q are positive integers whose greatest common factor is 1.

Then the equation $x^2 = 3$ becomes

$$p^2 = 3q^2.$$

Now p is either divisible by 3 or has remainder 1 or 2 on division by 3; that is, $p = 3k$ or $3k + 1$ or $3k + 2$ for some integer k.

But if $p = 3k + 1$, then $p^2 = 9k^2 + 6k + 1$ is not divisible by 3, and if $p = 3k + 2$, then

$$p^2 = 9k^2 + 12k + 4 = 3(3k^2 + 4k + 1) + 1$$

is not divisible by 3. So, since $3q^2$ is divisible by 3, we conclude that $p = 3k$.

Hence $(3k)^2 = 3q^2$, so $q^2 = 3k^2$.

But then the same argument applies to q to show that q must also be divisible by 3.

Hence 3 is a common factor of p and q.

This is a contradiction, so we conclude that the assumption must have been false. Hence there is no rational number x such that $x^2 = 3$.

2.1 (a) The equation $z^2 - 4z + 7 = 0$ has solutions
$$z = \frac{4 \pm \sqrt{16-28}}{2} = \frac{4 \pm \sqrt{-12}}{2} = 2 \pm \frac{i\sqrt{12}}{2}$$
$$= 2 \pm i\sqrt{3};$$

that is, $z = 2 + i\sqrt{3}$ and $z = 2 - i\sqrt{3}$.

(b) The equation $z^2 - iz + 2 = 0$ has solutions
$$z = \frac{i \pm \sqrt{i^2-8}}{2} = \frac{i}{2} \pm \frac{\sqrt{-9}}{2} = \frac{i}{2} \pm \frac{3i}{2};$$

that is, $z = 2i$ and $z = -i$.

(c) We can factorise the equation
$$z^3 - 3z^2 + 4z - 2 = 0$$
as
$$(z - 1)(z^2 - 2z + 2) = 0.$$
Hence $z = 1$ or $z = \dfrac{2 \pm \sqrt{4 - 8}}{2} = 1 \pm i$, so the
solutions are $z = 1$, $z = 1 + i$ and $z = 1 - i$.

(d) $z^4 - 16 = 0$ can be factorised as
$$(z^2 - 4)(z^2 + 4) = 0$$
giving $z^2 = 4$ or $z^2 = -4$.
Hence $z = 2$ or $z = -2$ or $z = 2i$ or $z = -2i$.

2.2

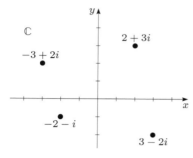

2.3 **(a)** $(3 - 5i) + (2 + 4i) = 5 - i$

(b) $(2 - 3i)(-3 + 2i) = -6 + 9i + 4i - 6i^2 = 13i$

(c) $(5 + 3i)^2 = (5 + 3i)(5 + 3i)$
$$= 25 + 15i + 15i + 9i^2$$
$$= 16 + 30i$$

(d) We find
$$(1 + i)(7 + 2i) = 7 + 7i + 2i + 2i^2 = 5 + 9i,$$
so
$$(1 + i)(7 + 2i)(4 - i) = (5 + 9i)(4 - i)$$
$$= 20 + 36i - 5i - 9i^2$$
$$= 29 + 31i.$$

2.4 $\overline{z_1} = -2 - 3i$ and $\overline{z_2} = 3 + i$.

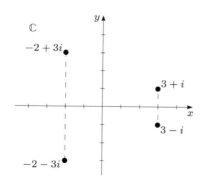

2.5 *Property 2*

Let $z_1 = x_1 + iy_1$ and $z_2 = x_2 + iy_2$. Then
$$z_1 z_2 = (x_1 + iy_1)(x_2 + iy_2)$$
$$= x_1 x_2 + i x_2 y_1 + i x_1 y_2 + i^2 y_1 y_2$$
$$= (x_1 x_2 - y_1 y_2) + i(x_2 y_1 + x_1 y_2),$$
so
$$\overline{z_1 z_2} = (x_1 x_2 - y_1 y_2) - i(x_2 y_1 + x_1 y_2).$$

Also,
$$\overline{z_1} \cdot \overline{z_2} = (x_1 - iy_1)(x_2 - iy_2)$$
$$= x_1 x_2 - i x_2 y_1 - i x_1 y_2 + i^2 y_1 y_2$$
$$= (x_1 x_2 - y_1 y_2) - i(x_2 y_1 + x_1 y_2).$$
Therefore
$$\overline{z_1 z_2} = \overline{z_1} \cdot \overline{z_2}.$$

Property 3

Let $z = x + iy$. Then
$$z + \overline{z} = x + iy + x - iy$$
$$= 2x$$
$$= 2 \operatorname{Re} z.$$

Property 4

Let $z = x + iy$. Then
$$z - \overline{z} = x + iy - (x - iy)$$
$$= 2iy$$
$$= 2i \operatorname{Im} z.$$

2.6 **(a)** $|5 + 12i| = \sqrt{5^2 + 12^2} = \sqrt{169} = 13$

(b) $|1 + i| = \sqrt{1^2 + 1^2} = \sqrt{2}$

(c) $|-5| = \sqrt{(-5)^2 + 0^2} = 5$

2.7 **(a)**

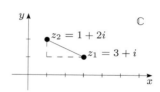

Here
$$z_1 - z_2 = (3 + i) - (1 + 2i) = 2 - i,$$
so
$$|z_1 - z_2| = \sqrt{2^2 + (-1)^2} = \sqrt{5}.$$

(b)

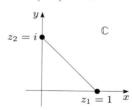

Here
$$z_1 - z_2 = 1 - i,$$
so
$$|z_1 - z_2| = \sqrt{1^2 + (-1)^2} = \sqrt{2}.$$

(c)

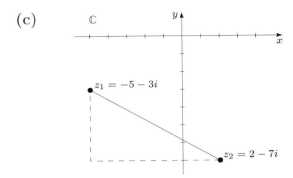

Here

$$z_1 - z_2 = (-5 - 3i) - (2 - 7i) = -7 + 4i,$$

so

$$|z_1 - z_2| = \sqrt{(-7)^2 + 4^2} = \sqrt{65}.$$

2.8 In each case we multiply both the numerator and the denominator by the complex conjugate of the denominator.

(a) $\dfrac{1}{3-i} = \dfrac{3+i}{(3-i)(3+i)}$

$\qquad = \dfrac{3+i}{3^2 + (-1)^2}$

$\qquad = \tfrac{3}{10} + \tfrac{1}{10}i$

(b) $\dfrac{1}{-1+2i} = \dfrac{-1-2i}{(-1+2i)(-1-2i)}$

$\qquad = \dfrac{-1-2i}{(-1)^2 + 2^2}$

$\qquad = -\tfrac{1}{5} - \tfrac{2}{5}i$

2.9 In each case we multiply the numerator and denominator by the complex conjugate of the denominator.

(a) $\dfrac{5}{2-i} = \dfrac{5 \times (2+i)}{(2-i) \times (2+i)}$

$\qquad = \dfrac{10 + 5i}{2^2 + 1^2}$

$\qquad = 2 + i$

(b) $\dfrac{2+3i}{-3+4i} = \dfrac{(2+3i) \times (-3-4i)}{(-3+4i) \times (-3-4i)}$

$\qquad = \dfrac{6 - 17i}{(-3)^2 + 4^2}$

$\qquad = \tfrac{6}{25} - \tfrac{17}{25}i$

2.10 (a) The required form is $x + iy$, where

$$x = 2\cos(\pi/2) = 0$$

and

$$y = 2\sin(\pi/2) = 2.$$

The Cartesian form is therefore $2i$.

(b) The required form is $x + iy$, where

$$x = 4\cos(-2\pi/3) = 4\cos(2\pi/3)$$
$$= -4\cos(\pi/3) = -2$$

and

$$y = 4\sin(-2\pi/3) = -4\sin(2\pi/3)$$
$$= -4\sin(\pi/3) = -2\sqrt{3}.$$

The Cartesian form is therefore $-2 - 2\sqrt{3}i$.

2.11 (a) Let $z = x + iy = -1 + i$, so $x = -1$ and $y = 1$. Then $z = r(\cos\theta + i\sin\theta)$, where

$$r = \sqrt{(-1)^2 + 1^2} = \sqrt{2}.$$

Also

$$\cos\phi = \frac{|x|}{r} = \frac{1}{\sqrt{2}}.$$

So $\phi = \pi/4$, and z lies in the second quadrant, so $\theta = \pi - \phi = 3\pi/4$.

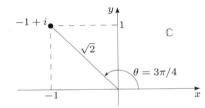

Thus the polar form of $-1 + i$ in terms of the principal argument is

$$\sqrt{2}(\cos(3\pi/4) + i\sin(3\pi/4)).$$

(b) Let $z = x + iy = 1 - \sqrt{3}i$, so $x = 1$ and $y = -\sqrt{3}$. Then $z = r(\cos\theta + i\sin\theta)$, where

$$r = \sqrt{1^2 + (-\sqrt{3})^2} = 2.$$

Also

$$\cos\phi = \frac{|x|}{r} = \frac{1}{2}.$$

So $\phi = \pi/3$, and z lies in the fourth quadrant, so $\theta = -\phi = -\pi/3$.

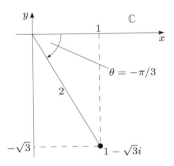

Thus the polar form of $1 - \sqrt{3}i$ in terms of the principal argument is

$$2(\cos(-\pi/3) + i\sin(-\pi/3)).$$

(c) Let $z = x + iy = -5$, so $x = -5$ and $y = 0$. Then $z = r(\cos\theta + i\sin\theta)$, where

$$r = \sqrt{(-5)^2 + 0^2} = 5.$$

Also z lies on the negative half of the real axis, so $\theta = \pi$.

Thus the polar form of -5 in terms of the principal argument is

$$5(\cos \pi + i \sin \pi).$$

2.12 (a) The modulus of the product is

$$4 \times \tfrac{1}{2} = 2.$$

An argument is

$$-\tfrac{1}{6}\pi + \tfrac{7}{8}\pi = \tfrac{17}{24}\pi.$$

Since this argument lies in $(-\pi, \pi]$, it follows that it is the principal argument. The required product is therefore

$$2\left(\cos(\tfrac{17}{24}\pi) + i \sin(\tfrac{17}{24}\pi)\right).$$

(b) The modulus of the product is

$$3 \times \tfrac{1}{2} = \tfrac{3}{2}.$$

An argument is

$$\tfrac{2}{3}\pi + \tfrac{1}{2}\pi = \tfrac{7}{6}\pi.$$

The principal argument is therefore

$$\tfrac{7}{6}\pi - 2\pi = -\tfrac{5}{6}\pi.$$

The required product is therefore

$$\tfrac{3}{2}\left(\cos(-\tfrac{5}{6}\pi) + i \sin(-\tfrac{5}{6}\pi)\right).$$

(c) The modulus of the quotient is

$$4 \div \tfrac{1}{2} = 8.$$

An argument is

$$-\tfrac{1}{6}\pi - \tfrac{7}{8}\pi = -\tfrac{25}{24}\pi.$$

The principal argument is therefore

$$-\tfrac{25}{24}\pi + 2\pi = \tfrac{23}{24}\pi.$$

The required quotient is therefore

$$8\left(\cos(\tfrac{23}{24}\pi) + i \sin(\tfrac{23}{24}\pi)\right).$$

(d) The modulus of the quotient is

$$3 \div \tfrac{1}{2} = 6.$$

An argument is

$$\tfrac{2}{3}\pi - \tfrac{1}{2}\pi = \tfrac{1}{6}\pi.$$

Since this argument lies in $(-\pi, \pi]$, it follows that it is the principal argument. The required quotient is therefore

$$6\left(\cos(\tfrac{1}{6}\pi) + i \sin(\tfrac{1}{6}\pi)\right).$$

2.13 From the solution to Exercise 2.11,

$$z_1 = \sqrt{2}(\cos \tfrac{3}{4}\pi + i \sin \tfrac{3}{4}\pi),$$

$$z_2 = 2\left(\cos(-\tfrac{1}{3}\pi) + i \sin(-\tfrac{1}{3}\pi)\right),$$

$$z_3 = 5(\cos \pi + i \sin \pi).$$

Hence

$$z_1 z_2 z_3 = 10\sqrt{2}\left(\cos(\tfrac{3}{4}\pi - \tfrac{1}{3}\pi + \pi)\right.$$
$$\left. + i \sin(\tfrac{3}{4}\pi - \tfrac{1}{3}\pi + \pi)\right)$$
$$= 10\sqrt{2}(\cos \tfrac{17}{12}\pi + i \sin \tfrac{17}{12}\pi)$$
$$= 10\sqrt{2}\left(\cos(-\tfrac{7}{12}\pi) + i \sin(-\tfrac{7}{12}\pi)\right),$$

using the principal argument.

Also

$$\frac{z_2 z_3}{z_1} = \frac{10}{\sqrt{2}}\left(\cos\left(-\tfrac{1}{3}\pi + \pi - \tfrac{3}{4}\pi\right)\right.$$
$$\left. + i \sin\left(-\tfrac{1}{3}\pi + \pi - \tfrac{3}{4}\pi\right)\right)$$
$$= 5\sqrt{2}\left(\cos(-\tfrac{1}{12}\pi) + i \sin(-\tfrac{1}{12}\pi)\right).$$

2.14 (a) $1 = 1(\cos 0 + i \sin 0)$

(b) If $z_1 = 1(\cos 0 + i \sin 0)$, then

$$z_1^3 = 1^3(\cos 0 + i \sin 0) = 1.$$

If $z_2 = 1(\cos \tfrac{2}{3}\pi + i \sin \tfrac{2}{3}\pi)$, then

$$z_2^3 = 1^3(\cos 2\pi + i \sin 2\pi) = 1.$$

If $z_3 = 1(\cos \tfrac{4}{3}\pi + i \sin \tfrac{4}{3}\pi)$, then

$$z_3^3 = 1^3(\cos 4\pi + i \sin 4\pi) = 1.$$

(c) In Cartesian form,

$$z_1 = 1,$$

$$z_2 = -\frac{1}{2} + i\frac{\sqrt{3}}{2},$$

$$z_3 = -\frac{1}{2} - i\frac{\sqrt{3}}{2}.$$

2.15 (a) Let $z = r(\cos \theta + i \sin \theta)$. Then, since

$$1 = 1(\cos 0 + i \sin 0),$$

we have

$$z^6 = r^6(\cos(6\theta) + i \sin(6\theta)) = 1(\cos 0 + i \sin 0).$$

(b) Hence $r = 1^{1/6} = 1$ and $\theta = 0 + \dfrac{2k\pi}{6}$ for $k = 0, 1, \ldots, 5$, and the six solutions of $z^6 = 1$ are given by

$$z = 1\left(\cos \frac{2k\pi}{6} + i \sin \frac{2k\pi}{6}\right) \text{ for } k = 0, 1, \ldots, 5.$$

Hence the solutions are

$$z_1 = 1(\cos 0 + i \sin 0),$$

$$z_2 = 1(\cos \tfrac{1}{3}\pi + i \sin \tfrac{1}{3}\pi),$$

$$z_3 = 1(\cos \tfrac{2}{3}\pi + i \sin \tfrac{2}{3}\pi),$$

$$z_4 = 1(\cos \pi + i \sin \pi),$$

$$z_5 = 1(\cos \tfrac{4}{3}\pi + i \sin \tfrac{4}{3}\pi),$$

$$z_6 = 1(\cos \tfrac{5}{3}\pi + i \sin \tfrac{5}{3}\pi).$$

(c)

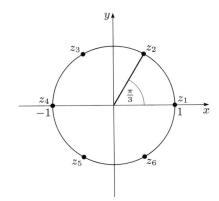

(d) $z_1 = 1,$

$z_2 = \dfrac{1}{2} + i\dfrac{\sqrt{3}}{2},$

$z_3 = -\dfrac{1}{2} + i\dfrac{\sqrt{3}}{2},$

$z_4 = -1,$

$z_5 = -\dfrac{1}{2} - i\dfrac{\sqrt{3}}{3},$

$z_6 = \dfrac{1}{2} - i\dfrac{\sqrt{3}}{2}.$

2.16 Let $z = r(\cos\theta + i\sin\theta)$. Then, since

$-4 = 4(\cos\pi + i\sin\pi),$

we have

$z^4 = r^4(\cos 4\theta + i\sin 4\theta) = 4(\cos\pi + i\sin\pi).$

Hence $r = 4^{1/4} = \sqrt{2}$ and $\theta = \dfrac{\pi}{4} + \dfrac{2k\pi}{4}$ for $k = 0, 1, 2, 3$.

So the solutions are

$z_1 = \sqrt{2}(\cos\tfrac{1}{4}\pi + i\sin\tfrac{1}{4}\pi) = 1 + i,$

$z_2 = \sqrt{2}(\cos\tfrac{3}{4}\pi + i\sin\tfrac{3}{4}\pi) = -1 + i,$

$z_3 = \sqrt{2}(\cos\tfrac{5}{4}\pi + i\sin\tfrac{5}{4}\pi) = -1 - i,$

$z_4 = \sqrt{2}(\cos\tfrac{7}{4}\pi + i\sin\tfrac{7}{4}\pi) = 1 - i.$

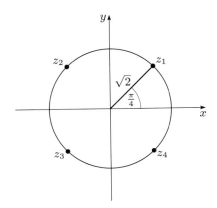

2.17 Let $z = r(\cos\theta + i\sin\theta)$.

Since $8i = 8\cos\tfrac{1}{2}\pi + i\sin\tfrac{1}{2}\pi$, we have

$z^3 = r^3(\cos 3\theta + i\sin 3\theta)$
$= 8\left(\cos\tfrac{1}{2}\pi + i\sin\tfrac{1}{2}\pi\right).$

Hence $r = 8^{1/3} = 2$ and $\theta = \dfrac{\pi}{6} + \dfrac{2k\pi}{3}$ for $k = 0, 1, 2$.

So the solutions are

$z_1 = 2\left(\cos\tfrac{1}{6}\pi + i\sin\tfrac{1}{6}\pi\right) = \sqrt{3} + i,$

$z_2 = 2\left(\cos\tfrac{5}{6}\pi + i\sin\tfrac{5}{6}\pi\right) = -\sqrt{3} + i,$

$z_3 = 2\left(\cos\tfrac{3}{2}\pi + i\sin\tfrac{3}{2}\pi\right) = -2i.$

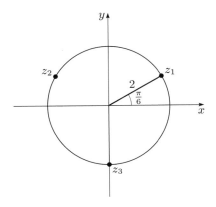

2.18 A suitable polynomial is

$(z - 1)(z + 2)(z - 3i)(z + 3i),$

that is,

$(z^2 + z - 2)(z^2 + 9)$

or

$z^4 + z^3 + 7z^2 + 9z - 18.$

2.19 (a) $(\cos\theta + i\sin\theta)^3$
$= (\cos\theta)^3 + 3(\cos\theta)^2(i\sin\theta)$
$\quad + 3(\cos\theta)(i\sin\theta)^2 + (i\sin\theta)^3$
$= \cos^3\theta + 3i\cos^2\theta\sin\theta - 3\cos\theta\sin^2\theta - i\sin^3\theta$
$= (\cos^3\theta - 3\cos\theta\sin^2\theta) + i(3\cos^2\theta\sin\theta - \sin^3\theta)$

(b) By part (a),

$\cos 3\theta + i\sin 3\theta = (\cos^3\theta - 3\cos\theta\sin^2\theta)$
$\qquad\qquad\qquad + i(3\cos^2\theta\sin\theta - \sin^3\theta),$

so

$\cos 3\theta = \cos^3\theta - 3\cos\theta\sin^2\theta$

and

$\sin 3\theta = 3\cos^2\theta\sin\theta - \sin^3\theta.$

(c) Since $\sin^2 \theta = 1 - \cos^2 \theta$ and $\cos^2 \theta = 1 - \sin^2 \theta$, we have

$$\cos 3\theta = \cos^3 \theta - 3\cos \theta(1 - \cos^2 \theta),$$

so

$$\cos 3\theta = 4\cos^3 \theta - 3\cos \theta,$$

and

$$\sin 3\theta = 3(1 - \sin^2 \theta)\sin \theta - \sin^3 \theta,$$

so

$$\sin 3\theta = 3\sin \theta - 4\sin^3 \theta.$$

2.20 (a) $\cos 5\theta + i \sin 5\theta$

$$= (\cos \theta + i\sin \theta)^5$$
$$= \cos^5 \theta + 5i\cos^4 \theta \sin \theta - 10\cos^3 \theta \sin^2 \theta$$
$$\quad - 10i\cos^2 \theta \sin^3 \theta + 5\cos \theta \sin^4 \theta + i\sin^5 \theta$$
$$= (\cos^5 \theta - 10\cos^3 \theta \sin^2 \theta + 5\cos \theta \sin^4 \theta)$$
$$\quad + i(5\cos^4 \theta \sin \theta - 10\cos^2 \theta \sin^3 \theta + \sin^5 \theta).$$

Equating real and imaginary parts gives

$$\cos 5\theta = \cos^5 \theta - 10\cos^3 \theta \sin^2 \theta + 5\cos \theta \sin^4 \theta$$

and

$$\sin 5\theta = 5\cos^4 \theta \sin \theta - 10\cos^2 \theta \sin^3 \theta + \sin^5 \theta.$$

(b) Since $\sin^2 \theta = 1 - \cos^2 \theta$ and $\sin^4 \theta = (\sin^2 \theta)^2 = (1 - \cos^2 \theta)^2$, on substituting into the formula for $\cos 5\theta$ found in part (b) we obtain

$$\cos 5\theta = \cos^5 \theta - 10\cos^3 \theta(1 - \cos^2 \theta)$$
$$\quad + 5\cos \theta(1 - \cos^2 \theta)^2$$
$$= \cos^5 \theta - 10\cos^3 \theta + 10\cos^5 \theta$$
$$\quad + 5\cos \theta - 10\cos^3 \theta + 5\cos^5 \theta,$$

so

$$\cos 5\theta = 16\cos^5 \theta - 20\cos^3 \theta + 5\cos \theta.$$

Similarly,

$$\sin 5\theta = 5(1 - \sin^2 \theta)^2 \sin \theta$$
$$\quad - 10(1 - \sin^2 \theta)\sin^3 \theta + \sin^5 \theta$$
$$= 5\sin \theta - 10\sin^3 \theta + 5\sin^5 \theta$$
$$\quad - 10\sin^3 \theta + 10\sin^5 \theta + \sin^5 \theta,$$

so

$$\sin 5\theta = 5\sin \theta - 20\sin^3 \theta + 16\sin^5 \theta.$$

2.21 (a) Let $z = x + iy$; then

$$\frac{1}{e^z} = \frac{1}{e^{x+iy}}$$

$$\quad = \frac{1}{e^x(\cos y + i\sin y)} \quad \text{(by definition)}$$

$$\quad = e^{-x}(\cos y + i\sin y)^{-1}$$

$$\quad = e^{-x}(\cos(-y) + i\sin(-y))$$

(by de Moivre's Theorem with $n = -1$)

$$\quad = e^{-x+i(-y)} = e^{-z} \quad \text{(by definition)}.$$

(b) $\dfrac{e^{z_1}}{e^{z_2}} = e^{z_1} \times \dfrac{1}{e^{z_2}}$

$$\quad = e^{z_1}e^{-z_2} \quad \text{(by part (a))}$$
$$\quad = e^{z_1+(-z_2)} \quad \text{(by Example 2.8)}$$
$$\quad = e^{z_1-z_2}.$$

2.22 (a) $2i\sin \theta = e^{i\theta} - e^{-i\theta}$, so $(2i\sin \theta)^5 = (e^{i\theta} - e^{-i\theta})^5$.

Hence

$$\sin^5 \theta = \frac{1}{2^5 i^5}(e^{i\theta} - e^{-i\theta})^5$$
$$\quad = \frac{1}{2^5 i}(e^{i\theta} - e^{-i\theta})^5.$$

(b) $(e^{i\theta} - e^{-i\theta})^5$

$$= (e^{i\theta})^5 + 5(e^{i\theta})^4(-e^{-i\theta})$$
$$\quad + 10(e^{i\theta})^3(-e^{-i\theta})^2$$
$$\quad + 10(e^{i\theta})^2(-e^{-i\theta})^3 + 5(e^{i\theta})(-e^{-i\theta})^4$$
$$\quad + (-e^{-i\theta})^5$$
$$= e^{i5\theta} - 5e^{i3\theta} + 10e^{i\theta} - 10e^{-i\theta}$$
$$\quad + 5e^{-i3\theta} - e^{-i5\theta}.$$

Hence

$$\sin^5 \theta = \frac{1}{2^5 i}(e^{i5\theta} - 5e^{i3\theta} + 10e^{i\theta} - 10e^{-i\theta}$$
$$\quad + 5e^{-i3\theta} - e^{-i5\theta})$$
$$= \frac{1}{2^5 i}\left((e^{i5\theta} - e^{-i5\theta}) - 5(e^{i3\theta} - e^{-i3\theta})\right.$$
$$\quad \left. + 10(e^{i\theta} - e^{-i\theta})\right)$$
$$= \frac{1}{2^5 i}(2i\sin 5\theta - 5(2i\sin 3\theta) + 10(2i\sin \theta))$$
$$= \tfrac{1}{16}(\sin 5\theta - 5\sin 3\theta + 10\sin \theta).$$

2.23 $z_1 + z_2 = (2 + 3i) + (1 - 4i) = 3 - i.$

$$z_1 - z_2 = (2 + 3i) - (1 - 4i) = 1 + 7i.$$

$$z_1 z_2 = (2 + 3i)(1 - 4i) = 2 + 3i - 8i - 12i^2$$
$$\qquad\qquad = 14 - 5i.$$

$$\overline{z_1} = 2 - 3i.$$

$$\overline{z_2} = 1 + 4i.$$

$$\frac{z_1}{z_2} = \frac{2 + 3i}{1 - 4i} = \frac{(2 + 3i)(1 + 4i)}{(1 - 4i)(1 + 4i)} = \frac{-10 + 11i}{1 + 16}$$
$$\qquad = -\tfrac{10}{17} + \tfrac{11}{16}i.$$

$$\frac{1}{z_1} = \frac{1}{2 + 3i} = \frac{2 - 3i}{(2 + 3i)(2 - 3i)} = \frac{2 - 3i}{13}$$
$$\qquad = \tfrac{2}{13} - \tfrac{3}{13}i.$$

2.24

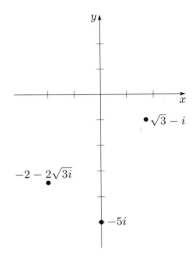

(a) Let $z = x + iy = \sqrt{3} - i$, so $x = \sqrt{3}$ and $y = -1$.
Then $z = r(\cos\theta + i\sin\theta)$, where

$$r = \sqrt{(\sqrt{3})^2 + (-1)^2} = 2.$$

Also $\cos\phi = \dfrac{|x|}{r} = \dfrac{\sqrt{3}}{2}$. So $\phi = \frac{1}{6}\pi$, and z lies in the fourth quadrant, so $\theta = -\phi = -\frac{1}{6}\pi$. Hence the polar form of $\sqrt{3} - i$ in terms of the principal argument is

$$2(\cos(-\tfrac{1}{6}\pi) + i\sin(-\tfrac{1}{6}\pi)).$$

(b) Let $z = x + iy = -5i$, so $x = 0$ and $y = -5$.
Then $z = r(\cos\theta + i\sin\theta)$, where

$$r = \sqrt{0^2 + (-5)^2} = 5.$$

Also z lies on the negative half of the imaginary axis, so $\theta = -\frac{1}{2}\pi$.
Hence the polar form of $-5i$ in terms of the principal argument is

$$5(\cos(-\tfrac{1}{2}\pi) + i\sin(-\tfrac{1}{2}\pi)).$$

(c) Let $z = x + iy = -2 - 2\sqrt{3}i$, so $x = -2$ and $y = -2\sqrt{3}$. Then $z = r(\cos\theta + i\sin\theta)$, where

$$r = \sqrt{(-2)^2 + (-2\sqrt{3})^2} = 4.$$

Also $\cos\phi = \dfrac{|x|}{r} = \frac{1}{2}$. So $\phi = \frac{1}{3}\pi$, and z lies in the third quadrant, so $\theta = -(\pi - \phi) = -\frac{2}{3}\pi$.
Hence the polar form of $-2 - 2\sqrt{3}i$ in terms of the principal argument is

$$4\left(\cos(-\tfrac{2}{3}\pi) + i\sin(-\tfrac{2}{3}\pi)\right).$$

2.25 **(a)** The required form is $x + iy$, where

$$x = 2\sqrt{2}\cos\tfrac{1}{4}\pi = 2\sqrt{2} \times \frac{1}{\sqrt{2}} = 2$$

and

$$y = 2\sqrt{2}\sin\tfrac{1}{4}\pi = 2\sqrt{2} \times \frac{1}{\sqrt{2}} = 2,$$

so the Cartesian form is $2 + 2i$.

(b) The required form is $x + iy$, where

$$x = 3\cos\tfrac{1}{2}\pi = 0 \quad \text{and} \quad y = 3\sin\tfrac{1}{2}\pi = 3,$$

so the Cartesian form is $3i$.

(c) The required form is $x + iy$, where

$$x = \cos\tfrac{5}{6}\pi = -\cos\tfrac{1}{6}\pi = -\frac{\sqrt{3}}{2}$$

and

$$y = \sin\tfrac{5}{6}\pi = \sin\tfrac{1}{6}\pi = \tfrac{1}{2},$$

so the Cartesian form is $-\dfrac{\sqrt{3}}{2} + \dfrac{1}{2}i$.

2.26 From the solution to Exercise 2.24, we have

$$z_1 = 2\left(\cos(-\tfrac{1}{6}\pi) + i\sin(-\tfrac{1}{6}\pi)\right),$$
$$z_2 = 5\left(\cos(-\tfrac{1}{2}\pi) + i\sin(-\tfrac{1}{2}\pi)\right),$$
$$z_3 = 4\left(\cos(-\tfrac{2}{3}\pi) + i\sin(-\tfrac{2}{3}\pi)\right).$$

(a) Hence

$$z_1 z_2 z_3 = 2 \times 5 \times 4\left(\cos(-\tfrac{1}{6}\pi - \tfrac{1}{2}\pi - \tfrac{2}{3}\pi)\right.$$
$$\left. + i\sin\left(-\tfrac{1}{6}\pi - \tfrac{1}{2}\pi - \tfrac{2}{3}\pi\right)\right)$$
$$= 40\left(\cos(-\tfrac{4}{3}\pi) + i\sin(-\tfrac{4}{3}\pi)\right)$$
$$= 40\left(\cos\tfrac{2}{3}\pi + i\sin\tfrac{2}{3}\pi\right),$$

using the principal argument.

(b) $\dfrac{z_1 z_2}{z_3} = \dfrac{2 \times 5}{4}\left(\cos(-\tfrac{1}{6}\pi - \tfrac{1}{2}\pi + \tfrac{2}{3}\pi)\right.$
$$\left. + i\sin\left(-\tfrac{1}{6}\pi - \tfrac{1}{2}\pi + \tfrac{2}{3}\pi\right)\right)$$
$$= \tfrac{5}{2}(\cos 0 + i\sin 0) = \tfrac{5}{2}.$$

2.27 Let $z = r(\cos\theta + i\sin\theta)$.
Then, since $-32 = 32(\cos\pi + i\sin\pi)$, we have

$$r^5(\cos 5\theta + i\sin 5\theta) = 32(\cos\pi + i\sin\pi).$$

Hence $r = 2$ and $\theta = \dfrac{\pi}{5} + \dfrac{2k\pi}{5}$ for any integer k, and the five solutions of $z^5 = -32$ are given by

$$z = 2\left(\cos\left(\frac{\pi}{5} + \frac{2k\pi}{5}\right) + i\sin\left(\frac{\pi}{5} + \frac{2k\pi}{5}\right)\right)$$

for $k = 0, 1, 2, 3, 4$.
Hence the solutions are

$$z_1 = 2\left(\cos\tfrac{1}{5}\pi + i\sin\tfrac{1}{5}\pi\right),$$
$$z_2 = 2\left(\cos\tfrac{3}{5}\pi + i\sin\tfrac{3}{5}\pi\right),$$
$$z_3 = 2(\cos\pi + i\sin\pi) = -2,$$
$$z_4 = 2\left(\cos\tfrac{7}{5}\pi + i\sin\tfrac{7}{5}\pi\right)$$
$$= 2\left(\cos\left(-\tfrac{3}{5}\pi\right) + i\sin\left(-\tfrac{3}{5}\pi\right)\right),$$
$$z_5 = 2\left(\cos\tfrac{9}{5}\pi + i\sin\tfrac{9}{5}\pi\right)$$
$$= 2\left(\cos\left(-\tfrac{1}{5}\pi\right) + i\sin\left(-\tfrac{1}{5}\pi\right)\right).$$

2.28 The integer solution must be a factor of the constant term 15, so it must be one of ± 1, ± 3, ± 5, ± 15. (See Unit I2, the discussion after the corollary to Theorem 4.3.)

Testing these, we find $z = -3$ is a root, since
$$(-3)^3 + (-3)^2 - (-3) + 15 = 0.$$
Hence $z + 3$ is a factor, and we find that
$$z^3 + z^2 - z + 15 = (z + 3)(z^2 - 2z + 5).$$
The solutions of $z^2 - 2z + 5 = 0$ are given by
$$z = \frac{2 \pm \sqrt{4 - 20}}{2} = \frac{2 \pm 4i}{2} = 1 \pm 2i.$$
Hence the solutions of $z^3 + z^2 - z + 15 = 0$ are $z = -3$, $z = 1 + 2i$ and $z = 1 - 2i$.

2.29 A suitable polynomial is
$$(z - 3)(z + 2)(z - (2 - i))(z - (2 + i)),$$
that is,
$$(z^2 - z - 6)(z^2 - 4z + 5)$$
or
$$z^4 - 5z^3 + 3z^2 + 19z - 30.$$

2.30 $\cos 6\theta + i \sin 6\theta = (\cos \theta + i \sin \theta)^6$
$$\begin{aligned}
&= \cos^6 \theta + 6i \cos^5 \theta \sin \theta + 15i^2 \cos^4 \theta \sin^2 \theta \\
&\quad + 20i^3 \cos^3 \theta \sin^3 \theta + 15i^4 \cos^2 \theta \sin^4 \theta \\
&\quad + 6i^5 \cos \theta \sin^5 \theta + i^6 \sin^6 \theta \\
&= \cos^6 \theta - 15 \cos^4 \theta \sin^2 \theta + 15 \cos^2 \theta \sin^4 \theta - \sin^6 \theta \\
&\quad + i(6 \cos^5 \theta \sin \theta - 20 \cos^3 \theta \sin^3 \theta + 6 \cos \theta \sin^5 \theta).
\end{aligned}$$
Hence
$$\begin{aligned}
\cos 6\theta = {}& \cos^6 \theta - 15 \cos^4 \theta \sin^2 \theta \\
&+ 15 \cos^2 \theta \sin^4 \theta - \sin^6 \theta
\end{aligned}$$
and
$$\begin{aligned}
\sin 6\theta = {}& 6 \cos^5 \theta \sin \theta - 20 \cos^3 \theta \sin^3 \theta \\
&+ 6 \cos \theta \sin^5 \theta.
\end{aligned}$$

2.31 (a) $e^{i\pi/2} = e^{0 + i\pi/2} = e^0(\cos(\tfrac{1}{2}\pi) + i \sin(\tfrac{1}{2}\pi))$
$$= 1(0 + i) = i.$$
(b) $e^{3 + i\pi/4} = e^3(\cos(\tfrac{1}{4}\pi) + i \sin(\tfrac{1}{4}\pi))$
$$= \frac{e^3}{\sqrt{2}} + i\frac{e^3}{\sqrt{2}}.$$
(c) $e^{-1 + i\pi} = e^{-1}(\cos \pi + i \sin \pi) = -e^{-1}.$

3.1 (a) $65 = 9 \times 7 + 2$, so the quotient is 9 and the remainder is 2.

(b) $-256 = -20 \times 13 + 4$, so the quotient is -20 and the remainder is 4.

3.2 (a) The possible remainders are 0, 1, 2, 3, 4, 5 and 6.

(b) There are many possible answers here; for example, 3, 10, -4 and -11.

3.3 We have
$$\begin{aligned}
25 &\equiv 8 \pmod{17}, \\
53 &\equiv 2 \pmod{17}, \\
-15 &\equiv 2 \pmod{17}, \\
3 &\equiv 3 \pmod{17}, \\
127 &\equiv 8 \pmod{17},
\end{aligned}$$
so the remainders are 8, 2, 2, 3 and 8, respectively. So $25 \equiv 127 \pmod{17}$ and $53 \equiv -15 \pmod{17}$.

3.4 (a) Suppose that $a \equiv b \pmod n$ and $c \equiv d \pmod n$. Then $a = b + kn$ and $c = d + ln$ for some integers k and l.

Hence
$$\begin{aligned}
ac &= (b + kn)(d + ln) \\
&= bd + bln + knd + kln^2 \\
&= bd + n(bl + kd + kln),
\end{aligned}$$
so $ac - bd = (bl + kd + kln)n$, so $ac \equiv bd \pmod n$.

(b) Suppose that $a \equiv b \pmod n$ and let $P(k)$ be the statement $a^k \equiv b^k \pmod n$.

Then $P(1)$ is true, since we know that $a \equiv b \pmod n$. Suppose that $r \geq 1$ and $P(r)$ is true, that is, $a^r \equiv b^r \pmod n$. Then, by property (e), since $a^r \equiv b^r$ and $a \equiv b \pmod n$, we have $a^r \times a \equiv b^r \times b \pmod n$, that is,
$$a^{r+1} \equiv b^{r+1} \pmod n.$$
Hence $P(r)$ true $\Rightarrow P(r + 1)$ true, so by mathematical induction $P(k)$ is true for all positive integers k.

3.5 (a) $3 +_5 7 = 0$, $4 +_{17} 5 = 9$, $8 +_{16} 12 = 4$.

(b) $3 \times_5 7 = 1$, $4 \times_{17} 5 = 3$, $8 \times_{16} 12 = 0$.

3.6 (a) (i) $3 +_4 3 = 2$, so $x = 3$.

(ii) $4 +_7 5 = 2$, so $x = 4$.

(iii) $2 +_4 2 = 0$, so $x = 2$.

(iv) $2 +_7 5 = 0$, so $x = 2$.

(b) You may have noticed that:

1. each element appears exactly once in each row and exactly once in each column;

2. there is a pattern of diagonal stripes running down from right to left.

3.7 (a)

$+_6$	0	1	2	3	4	5
0	0	1	2	3	4	5
1	1	2	3	4	5	0
2	2	3	4	5	0	1
3	3	4	5	0	1	2
4	4	5	0	1	2	3
5	5	0	1	2	3	4

(b) $x +_6 1 = 5$ has solution $x = 4$.

$x +_6 5 = 1$ has solution $x = 2$.

3.8 By definition, $a +_n b$ and $b +_n a$ are the remainders of $a + b$ and $b + a$, respectively, on division by n. But $a + b = b + a$, so $a +_n b = b +_n a$.

3.9 (a)

a	0	1	2	3	4	5	6
$-_7 a$	0	6	5	4	3	2	1

(b)

a	0	1	2	...	r	...	$n-1$
$-_n a$	0	$n-1$	$n-2$	...	$n-r$		1

The additive inverse of 0 is always 0, since $0 +_n 0 = 0$. For any integer $r > 0$ in $\mathbb{Z}_n$, $n - r \in \mathbb{Z}_n$ and $r + (n - r) = n$, so $r +_n (n - r) = 0$.

3.10 (a) (i) 1 and 3 have multiplicative inverses in $\mathbb{Z}_4$, since $1 \times_4 1 = 1$ and $3 \times_4 3 = 1$.

(ii) The multiplicative inverses in $\mathbb{Z}_7$ are given by the following table, where b is the multiplicative inverse of a.

a	1	2	3	4	5	6
b	1	4	5	2	3	6

(b)

$\times_{10}$	0	1	2	3	4	5	6	7	8	9
0	0	0	0	0	0	0	0	0	0	0
1	0	1	2	3	4	5	6	7	8	9
2	0	2	4	6	8	0	2	4	6	8
3	0	3	6	9	2	5	8	1	4	7
4	0	4	8	2	6	0	4	8	2	6
5	0	5	0	5	0	5	0	5	0	5
6	0	6	2	8	4	0	6	2	8	4
7	0	7	4	1	8	5	2	9	6	3
8	0	8	6	4	2	0	8	6	4	2
9	0	9	8	7	6	5	4	3	2	1

The integers 1, 3, 7 and 9 have multiplicative inverses in $\mathbb{Z}_{10}$.

3.11 (a) $16 = 2 \times 7 + 2$

$\qquad 7 = 3 \times 2 + 1$

Starting with the last equation, we have

$\begin{aligned} 1 &= 7 - 3 \times 2 \\ &= 7 - 3 \times (16 - 2 \times 7) \\ &= 7 \times 7 - 3 \times 16. \end{aligned}$

Hence $7 \times 7 = 3 \times 16 + 1$, so $7 \times_{16} 7 = 1$ and the multiplicative inverse of 7 in $\mathbb{Z}_{16}$ is 7.

(b) $51 = 6 \times 8 + 3$

$\qquad 8 = 2 \times 3 + 2$

$\qquad 3 = 1 \times 2 + 1$

Starting with the last equation, we have

$\begin{aligned} 1 &= 3 - 2 \\ &= 3 - (8 - 2 \times 3) \\ &= -8 + 3 \times 3 \\ &= -8 + 3 \times (51 - 6 \times 8) \\ &= 3 \times 51 - 19 \times 8. \end{aligned}$

Hence $(-19) \times 8 \equiv 1 \pmod{51}$, so

$(51 - 19) \times 8 \equiv 1 \pmod{51}$.

Hence $32 \times_{51} 8 = 1$ and the multiplicative inverse of 8 in $\mathbb{Z}_{51}$ is 32.

3.12 (a) Since the multiplicative inverse of 7 in $\mathbb{Z}_{16}$ is 7 (see the solution to Exercise 3.11(a)), we have

$\begin{aligned} 7 \times_{16} x = 3 &\Leftrightarrow 7 \times_{16} 7 \times_{16} x = 7 \times_{16} 3 \\ &\Leftrightarrow x = 5. \end{aligned}$

(b) Since the multiplicative inverse of 8 in $\mathbb{Z}_{51}$ is 32 (see the solution to Exercise 3.11(b)), we have

$\begin{aligned} 8 \times_{51} x = 19 &\Leftrightarrow 32 \times_{51} 8 \times_{51} x = 32 \times_{51} 19 \\ &\Leftrightarrow x = 47. \end{aligned}$ $\quad 32 \times 19 \div 51 \text{ o find rem}$

3.13 (a) One solution of the equation $3 \times_{12} x = 6$ is $x = 2$. Also $n/d = 12/3 = 4$, so the other solutions are $x = 2 + 4 = 6$ and $x = 2 + 2 \times 4 = 10$.

The equation $8 \times_{12} x = 7$ has no solutions because 8 and 12 have common factor 4 but 7 does not.

Because 5 and 12 are coprime, the equation $5 \times_{12} x = 2$ has a unique solution. The solution, $x = 10$, can be found in various ways: for example, by calculating $x = 5^{-1} \times_{12} 2$, or by testing possible values for x, or by spotting that $2 \equiv -10 \pmod{12}$ and using the fact that the congruence $5 \times (-2) \equiv -10 \pmod{12}$ implies $5 \times 10 \equiv 2 \pmod{12}$ giving $5 \times_{12} 10 = 2$.

(b) One solution of the equation $4 \times_{16} x = 12$ is $x = 3$. Also $n/d = 16/4 = 4$, so the other solutions are $x = 3 + 4 = 7$, $x = 3 + 8 = 11$ and $x = 3 + 12 = 15$.

Because 3 and 16 are coprime, the equation $3 \times_{16} x = 13$ has a unique solution. The solution, $x = 15$, can be found in various ways: for example, by calculating $x = 3^{-1} \times_{16} 13$, or by testing possible values for x, or by spotting that $13 \equiv -3 \pmod{16}$ and using the fact that the congruence $3 \times (-1) \equiv -3 \pmod{16}$ implies $3 \times 15 \equiv 13 \pmod{16}$ giving $3 \times_{16} 15 = 13$.

The equation $8 \times_{16} x = 2$ has no solutions because 8 and 16 have common factor 4 but 2 does not.

3.14 We find all the values of $x \times_8 x$.

x	0	1	2	3	4	5	6	7
$x \times_8 x$	0	1	4	1	0	1	4	1

(a) The solutions of $x \times_8 x = 4$ are $x = 2$ and $x = 6$.

(b) The equation $x \times_8 x = c$ can be solved for $c = 0, 1, 4$.

3.15 (a) $21 +_{26} 15 = 10, \quad 21 \times_{26} 15 = 3$.

(b) $19 +_{33} 14 = 0, \quad 19 \times_{33} 14 = 2$.

3.16 (a)
$$21 = 2 \times 8 + 5$$
$$8 = 1 \times 5 + 3$$
$$5 = 1 \times 3 + 2$$
$$3 = 1 \times 2 + 1$$

Hence
$$
\begin{aligned}
1 &= 3 - 1 \times 2 \\
&= 3 - (5 - 3) \\
&= -5 + 2 \times 3 \\
&= -5 + 2 \times (8 - 5) \\
&= 2 \times 8 - 3 \times 5 \\
&= 2 \times 8 - 3 \times (21 - 2 \times 8) \\
&= -3 \times 21 + 8 \times 8.
\end{aligned}
$$
Hence $8 \times 8 = 3 \times 21 + 1$, so
$$8 \times_{21} 8 = 1,$$
so the multiplicative inverse of 8 in $\mathbb{Z}_{21}$ is 8.

(b)
$$33 = 1 \times 19 + 14$$
$$19 = 1 \times 14 + 5$$
$$14 = 2 \times 5 + 4$$
$$5 = 1 \times 4 + 1$$

Hence
$$
\begin{aligned}
1 &= 5 - 4 \\
&= 5 - (14 - 2 \times 5) \\
&= -14 + 3 \times 5 \\
&= -14 + 3 \times (19 - 14) \\
&= 3 \times 19 - 4 \times 14 \\
&= 3 \times 19 - 4 \times (33 - 19) \\
&= -4 \times 33 + 7 \times 19.
\end{aligned}
$$

Hence
$$7 \times 19 = 4 \times 33 + 1,$$
so
$$7 \times_{33} 19 = 1,$$
so the multiplicative inverse of 19 in $\mathbb{Z}_{33}$ is 7.

3.17

$\times_{11}$	0	1	2	3	4	5	6	7	8	9	10
0	0	0	0	0	0	0	0	0	0	0	0
1	0	1	2	3	4	5	6	7	8	9	10
2	0	2	4	6	8	10	1	3	5	7	9
3	0	3	6	9	1	4	7	10	2	5	8
4	0	4	8	1	5	9	2	6	10	3	7
5	0	5	10	4	9	3	8	2	7	1	6
6	0	6	1	7	2	8	3	9	4	10	5
7	0	7	3	10	6	2	9	5	1	8	4
8	0	8	5	2	10	7	4	1	9	6	3
9	0	9	7	5	3	1	10	8	6	4	2
10	0	10	9	8	7	6	5	4	3	2	1

Hence we have the following multiplicative inverses in $\mathbb{Z}_{11}$.

x	1	2	3	4	5	6	7	8	9	10
x^{-1}	1	6	4	3	9	2	8	7	5	10

3.18 (a) We have $8 \times_{21} x = 13$. Multiplying by 8, which is the multiplicative inverse of 8 mod 21 (see the solution to Exercise 3.16(a)), we have
$$8 \times_{21} (8 \times_{21} x) = 8 \times_{21} 13,$$
so
$$x = 8 \times_{21} 13 = 20.$$

(b) We have $19 \times_{33} x = 15$. Multiplying by 7, which is the multiplicative inverse of 19 mod 33 (see the solution to Exercise 3.16(b)), we have
$$7 \times_{33} (19 \times_{33} x) = 7 \times_{33} 15,$$
so
$$x = 7 \times_{33} 15 = 6.$$

3.19 (a) Because 3 and 8 are coprime, the equation $3 \times_8 x = 7$ has a unique solution. The solution, $x = 5$, can be found in various ways: for example, by calculating $x = 3^{-1} \times_8 7$, or by testing possible values for x, or by spotting that $7 \equiv 15 \pmod{8}$ and using the fact that the congruence $3 \times 5 \equiv 15 \pmod{8}$ implies $3 \times 5 \equiv 7 \pmod{8}$ giving $3 \times_8 5 = 7$.

The equation $4 \times_8 x = 7$ has no solutions because 4 and 8 have common factor 4 but 7 does not.

One solution of the equation $4 \times_8 x = 4$ is $x = 1$. Also $n/d = 8/4 = 2$, so the other solutions are $x = 1 + 2 = 3$, $x = 1 + 4 = 5$ and $x = 1 + 6 = 7$.

(b) One solution of the equation $3 \times_{15} x = 6$ is $x = 2$. Also $n/d = 15/3 = 5$, so the other solutions are $x = 2 + 5 = 7$ and $x = 2 + 10 = 12$.

Because 4 and 15 are coprime, the equation $4 \times_{15} x = 3$ has a unique solution. The solution, $x = 12$, can be found in various ways: for example, by calculating $x = 4^{-1} \times_{15} 3$, or by testing possible values for x, or by spotting that $3 \equiv -12 \pmod{15}$ and using the fact that the congruence $4 \times (-3) \equiv -12 \pmod{15}$ implies $4 \times 12 \equiv 3 \pmod{15}$ giving $4 \times_{15} 12 = 3$.

The equation $5 \times_{15} x = 2$ has no solutions because 5 and 15 have common factor 5 but 2 does not.

3.20 We find all the values of $x \times_{12} x$.

x	0	1	2	3	4	5	6	7	8	9	10	11
$x \times_{12} x$	0	1	4	9	4	1	0	1	4	9	4	1

(a) Hence there is no integer $x \in \mathbb{Z}_{12}$ such that $x \times_{12} x = 7$.

(b) The solutions of $x \times_{12} x = 4$ are $x = 2, 4, 8, 10$.

4.1 (a) This relation is not reflexive; for example, $2 \nsim 2$ since $2 - 2 = 0$ which is not odd.

The relation is symmetric; if $x \sim y$ then $x - y$ is odd, so $y - x = -(x - y)$ is also odd, so $y \sim x$.

The relation is not transitive; for example, $5 \sim 2$ since $5 - 2$ is odd, $2 \sim 1$ since $2 - 1$ is odd, but $5 \nsim 1$ since $5 - 1$ is even.

The relation is not an equivalence relation.

(b) This relation is reflexive, since $x - x = 0$, which is even, for all $x \in \mathbb{Z}$.

It is symmetric, since if $x \sim y$, then $x - y$ is even, so $y - x = -(x - y)$ is even, so $y \sim x$.

It is transitive, since if $x \sim y$ and $y \sim z$, then $x - y$ is even and $y - z$ is even, so $x - z = x - y + y - z$ is the sum of two even numbers, so is even, so $x \sim z$.

The relation is an equivalence relation.

(c) Any line ℓ is parallel to itself, so this relation is reflexive.

It is symmetric, since if ℓ_1 is parallel to ℓ_2, then ℓ_2 is parallel to ℓ_1.

It is transitive, since if ℓ_1 is parallel to ℓ_2 and ℓ_2 is parallel to ℓ_3, then ℓ_1 is parallel to ℓ_3.

The relation is an equivalence relation.

(d) This relation is reflexive, since for all $z \in \mathbb{C}$ we have $z - z = 0$, which is real, so $z \sim z$.

It is symmetric, since if $z_1 - z_2$ is real, then $z_2 - z_1 = -(z_1 - z_2)$ is also real.

It is transitive because, if $z_1 - z_2$ is real and $z_2 - z_3$ is real, then $z_1 - z_3 = z_1 - z_2 + z_2 - z_3$ is the sum of two real numbers and so is real.

The relation is an equivalence relation.

4.2 For the equivalence relation in Exercise 4.1(b), the equivalence class $[\![m]\!]$ of a particular integer $m \in \mathbb{Z}$ is the set of integers that differ from m by an even integer. That is,

$$[\![m]\!] = \{\ldots, m - 4, m - 2, m, m + 2, m + 4, \ldots\}.$$

In particular,

$$[\![0]\!] = \{\ldots, -4, -2, 0, 2, 4, \ldots\},$$
$$[\![1]\!] = \{\ldots, -3, -1, 1, 3, 5, \ldots\}.$$

These are the only equivalence classes (since the equivalence class of any other integer is equal to one of these two). So the equivalence classes are the even integers and the odd integers.

For the equivalence relation in Exercise 4.1(c), the equivalence class of a particular line is the set of all lines that are parallel to that line. So each equivalence class consists of all lines with a particular gradient. For example, all vertical lines form one equivalence class, and all lines with gradient 3 form another.

For the equivalence relation in Exercise 4.1(d), the equivalence class of a particular complex number $z_0 \in \mathbb{C}$ is

$$[\![z_0]\!] = \{z \in \mathbb{C} : z_0 - z \text{ is real}\}.$$

If $z_0 = x_0 + iy_0$ and $z = x + iy$, then

$$z_0 - z = (x_0 - x) + i(y_0 - y),$$

which is a real number if and only if $y = y_0$. Thus $[\![z_0]\!]$ consists of all complex numbers with the same imaginary part as z_0. So each equivalence class consists of all complex numbers with a particular imaginary part. For example, all complex numbers of the form $x + 3i$, where $x \in \mathbb{R}$, form one equivalence class, and all complex numbers of the form $x - \pi i$, where $x \in \mathbb{R}$, form another. The equivalence classes thus form horizontal lines in the complex plane.

Remark These solutions are quite detailed, but you may find that you can determine equivalence classes with less working as you become more familiar with them.

4.3 $\sim$ is not reflexive because, for example, $1 \nsim 1$ since $2 \times 1 - 1 = 1$ is not divisible by 7.

$\sim$ is not symmetric because, for example, $5 \sim 3$ since $2 \times 5 - 3 = 7$ which is divisible by 7, but $3 \nsim 5$ since $2 \times 3 - 5 = 1$ which is not divisible by 7.

$\sim$ is not transitive because, for example, $5 \sim 3$ and $3 \sim 6$ since $2 \times 5 - 3 = 7$ and $2 \times 3 - 6 = 0$ which are both divisible by 7, but $5 \nsim 6$ since $2 \times 5 - 6 = 4$ which is not divisible by 7.

4.4 We show that properties E1, E2 and E3 hold.

E1   For any function $f : \mathbb{R} \to \mathbb{R}$, $f(0) = f(0)$, so $f \sim f$ and hence the relation is reflexive.

E2   If $f \sim g$ so that $f(0) = g(0)$, then $g(0) = f(0)$, so $g \sim f$ and hence the relation is symmetric.

E3   If $f \sim g$ and $g \sim h$ so that $f(0) = g(0)$ and $g(0) = h(0)$, then $f(0) = h(0)$, so $f \sim h$ and hence the relation is transitive.

Therefore this is an equivalence relation.

Each equivalence class consists of all functions in A that take a particular value at 0; that is, each equivalence class is of the form

$$\{f \in A : f(0) = r\},$$

for some $r \in \mathbb{R}$.

4.5 We show that properties E1, E2 and E3 hold.

E1   Let $z = x + iy \in \mathbb{C}$. Then

$$x - x = 0 = 5(y - y),$$

so $z \sim z$. Hence the relation is reflexive.

E2   Let $z_1 = x_1 + iy_1$ and $z_2 = x_2 + iy_2$ be elements of $\mathbb{C}$. Suppose that $z_1 \sim z_2$ so that $x_1 - x_2 = 5(y_1 - y_2)$. Then

$$
\begin{aligned}
x_2 - x_1 &= -(x_1 - x_2) \\
&= -5(y_1 - y_2) \\
&= 5(y_2 - y_1),
\end{aligned}
$$

so $z_2 \sim z_1$. Hence the relation is symmetric.

E3   Let $z_3 = x_3 + iy_3$, and suppose that $z_1 \sim z_2$ and $z_2 \sim z_3$ so that

$$x_1 - x_2 = 5(y_1 - y_2)$$

and

$$x_2 - x_3 = 5(y_2 - y_3).$$

Then

$$
\begin{aligned}
x_1 - x_3 &= x_1 - x_2 + x_2 - x_3 \\
&= 5(y_1 - y_2) + 5(y_2 - y_3) \\
&= 5(y_1 - y_3),
\end{aligned}
$$

so $z_1 \sim z_3$. Hence the relation is transitive.

Therefore this is an equivalence relation.

Two complex numbers $x_1 + iy_1$ and $x_2 + iy_2$ are related by this relation if

$$x_1 - x_2 = 5(y_1 - y_2);$$

that is, if

$$x_1 - 5y_1 = x_2 - 5y_2.$$

Hence the equivalence classes are the lines $x - 5y = r$, for each real number r; that is, the lines with gradient $\frac{1}{5}$.

Index